Hand That's Dealt

By: Jayne Gongol

Jayne Gongol
Bob Begin

For Pearl
I kept my promise to you. B.B.

Button Box Survival

Prologue

To survive, one must have an old Christmas tin box, the outside of it decorated with ornate poinsettias and splotched with rust marks from being discarded on a corner basement floor among other junk items like broken fishing poles, rags, bicycle tires, and old newspapers, where it lives until one day tiny hands reach for it. In fact, the cemented basement floor is also where the father works his wood-magic into beautiful furniture and cabinet pieces. But it is the tin box that matters, not the numerous large, wood-cutting saws, the strips of new pine, walnut, and oak wood stacked against the wall, the shelves of little gadgets, screws and bolts, the dust that lingers on the floor after a day's work is completed. Inside the box are particularly important treasures like string, old nuts and bolts, pieces of broken pens, wire, tiny springs, staples, a stretch of measuring tape, buttons, needles, stones, rubber bands, magnets, and whatever else a young boy needs to survive. Only he uses the items in the precious bin to invent his own world, just by tinkering with string, winding wire to make a bird, the little miniature car, a moving pulley, and whatever he can invent and thus survive on his own terms without the outside world bashing at him. Cherish the tarnished box because it is the only thing that makes any sense in his senseless world. Without it, insignificant as it seems, despair is around the corner. Inside the box, his world can mercifully begin on his own terms. He places it before him, so he can thumb through it to find exactly what he needs to make the perfect sculpture, the perfect little animal or toy, using his hands and fingers. The tin button box has the secret ability to keep a little boy alive. It can overcome deprivation, bruises, broken bones, hunger, manipulation, and all the confusing wrongs in his world. The box is a matter of life over death, just an old Christmas tin box, buttons and all.

CHAPTER 1

In 1925, Pearl Roseman Ward was born in a small house in Middleton, Nova Scotia, on her Uncle Irving and Aunt May's farm. Alice, Pearl's mother, felt she had done her motherly duty by delivering a healthy infant and decided to leave her infant in the care of her sister and brother-in-law. In Nevada, she married a rich and lived an exciting life as the manager of a nightclub. When she discovered she was pregnant, she returned to her childhood home in Nova Scotia to have her baby in secret. All through her pregnancy, she had stayed with her sister and brother-in-law, hoping her blossoming abdomen would not ruin her shapely figure.

Aunt May performed all the duties required of mothers, feeding the infant, Pearl, cow's milk and diapering her as needed, while her sister, Alice, impatiently waited to recover, so she could return to her life in Nevada. The Canadian government gave May and Irving $50.00 a month to care for each orphan they kept at their residence, and they needed the children's help to run their farm efficiently. Subsiding entirely on what they could produce on their 100-acre farm meant they needed a lot of work hands.

When Alice recovered her curvaceous figure, she boarded the train out of Halifax and returned to her wealthy husband and their exciting, booze-filled life. But over the years, Alice would return to give May and Irving more babies she did not want. One was named Flora, who looked exactly like Pearl. In total, May and Irving raised 19 children on the farm, three boys of their own and some nieces and nephews, and others just orphans.

Pearl grew healthy. The farm work was hard, the winters long and cold, but she was well cared for and allowed to attend school. In the winter, she walked to school carrying a fire-heated slate she hid inside her coat to keep her hands and body warm. Wearing inadequate shoes, she trudged through four- to eight-inch-deep snow to reach the school. Often, she had to stop and press the hot slate to her frozen feet to warm them up. But she always made it to school. Farm life was hard, but she thrived. She loved to sing and had a dream of becoming a famous singer when she grew up. She was just a small girl, but when she opened her mouth, she sang like a grown opera singer with a full voice rich with experience and grown-up emotions. With her talented voice, her bright blue eyes above pronounced cheekbones, and some luck, she may have achieved that dream, but destiny had different goals for her.

She had just turned 18 years old when she met a dashing and charming sailor who came to Nova Scotia for a visit. Charles Robert Begin looked like quite the catch, and she was smitten. Only knowing the farm life, she was unaware of what lay beyond her limited parameters. Charles charmed her and promised her a good life in America. Falling prey to her budding, naive infatuation for a man she hardly knew and imagining the realization of her impossible singing career, she decided to marry him. Since she did not have any official record of her birth, she had to wait until the proper papers were processed before she could marry Charles.

When she finally arrived in America, she married her sailor and moved to Danvers, Massachusetts, to live with his parents, eight brothers, and two sisters. Pearl promptly became pregnant. By the time Robby was born in 1953, she already had two other daughters, Teresa and Nancy, and a son named Darin. Charles, her husband, had come home for visits but spent most of those early years away on secret missions during the Korean War, sneaking onto islands at night and building airstrip landings and then covering them up during the day to keep them hidden from the enemy. Charles' parents were abusive to their children. Pearl, adept at survival in the harsh Nova Scotia terrain, knew how to endure these circumstances and never gave up her dream to be a singer.

Everyone loved her singing voice. She modeled her musical voice after Mario Lanza's voice. He was her musical hero. While her husband was overseas, she found someone willing to record two of her songs and make a record for her. A photo of her sweet, young face was placed on the jacket cover. She hoped to have her songs played on the radio. But once Charles came home and saw what she had done, he forbade her to ever sing again. At sea for so long, he had missed most of his children's early years. He took one look at Robby, who had been born while he was gone and believed his wife had given birth to someone else's son. Robby, named Robert Emile Begin, did not look at all like him. All three of his other children looked like him, but Robby looked foreign, with blue eyes instead of brown like the others had feet that turned inward. His piercing eyes showed too much emotion for a boy. Charles would not claim him and made a point of continually accusing Pearl of having sex with another man on that damn Nova Scotia farm where all the men were screwing all the women, which made Pearl burst into tears. She knew the story was not true, but she also knew, even at that stage in her marriage, not to contradict her husband, or she would pay for it. Charles made it clear that she was completely under his control and would remain so.

She was mortified to see Charles turn his anger and rage onto Robby and then use the abuse as an example to make his other children behave. It was at that moment that Robby's childhood fate was sealed. He would endure most of his Father's wrath so his mother, three siblings, and the two to follow in later years would be spared.

CHAPTER 2

After his military service was completed, Robby's father secured a job at a chemical plant in Rhode Island. The Begin family bought a small house in East Riverside and settled in to raise their family in a small community of factory workers and mill plant workers. Although small, the neighborhood houses each had an indoor bathroom and three small bedrooms, along with a modest living room and kitchen. The owners planted trees and vegetable gardens. The town center was filled with car mechanics, merchandise stores, and grocery stores. Beyond the town's graveyard, near the river's bay, restaurants flourished with Italian families who served food recipes from the old country. When the wind blew in the summer, the stench of fish permeated the air around the town. No one complained in the 1950s about the air or about anything, for that matter. The families' lives were a significant improvement from the lives their ancestors had lived. People worked hard, endured the cold winters, basked in the sun's warmth in the summer, and paid no attention to the pollution pouring out of the smokestacks.

Robby was five years old when he was first taken to the farm in Nova Scotia to live for what would be several summers to come. His memories of the years before going to the farm were fleeting and filled with confusion. Few of them were positive. His foot turned inward and made him unable to walk correctly. His father called him a cripple. He often grabbed Robby by the leg and swung him around to belittle and hurt him. Robby had a long scar across his abdomen and was told he had survived a fiery house explosion as a baby that had lodged something foreign in his body. He was told his mother had rescued him, and he had surgery to repair the damage. He never questioned his mother's explanation. Daily, he endured verbal abuse and slaps from his father. He was slapped for just the simple pleasure of smiling. His father knocked Robby's head against the wall and often sharply backhanded him on the back of his neck. To control Robby, his father picked him up by one wrist and held his entire body off the floor, then slapped him over and over. He shook his little body, dismissing his son's obvious pain. When he finally dropped his son, Robby's shoulder was dislocated, and his entire shoulder bent. Robby staggered away, wobbling on his feet, falling, while his father acted as if it had never happened.

His father showed no emotions when he hurt Robby. His voice boomed. "You will bend to my will, Robby."

Robby's shoulder hurt. Yet, he could not cry out without facing severe retaliation. His father's behavior confounded and confused him. Often inside the house, his father smiled pleasantly and invited Robby over to him. Robby ran to his father, lured in by his father's invitation, thinking this was the day his father was going to show him some affection, only to be blindsided by a violent slap that would send him reeling. "If you have time to smile, you are not busy enough," he said to Robby.

His mother said, "Why do you hit Robby?"

"I'm knocking some sense into this kid," his father snapped at his wife.

Little Robby coiled away, shrinking into the invisibility of the walls as if he were part of it, slinking along the floors, winding along the baseboards, his hands flat against the walls. He lived in fear of his father, avoiding him at every turn, hiding in closets and under his bed, fearing the sound of his father's squeaking steps along the wood floors.

But, at five years old, Robby fought back. While lying on the sofa one day, watching television, his father marched over to him, leaned down, and picked him up. Robby thought his father may behave affectionately toward him. But then his father abruptly dropped him on the sofa. Robby was stunned. His father's pencil dropped out of his shirt pocket and landed on Robby's cheek, near the corner of his mouth. Robby reached for the pencil and gripped it. Before he could pull the pencil away, his father purposely pushed the pencil all through Robby's cheek and into his mouth. Robby cried out, stunned. He quickly reached his hand to his face, pulled the pencil out of his mouth, and stabbed his father's face with it so violently that the pencil penetrated his father's cheek too. His father stumbled backward. His anger completely dissolved into astonishment. He pulled the pencil out of his cheek. Blood ran down his face. Robby bolted up and raced into his bedroom. His heart pounding, he hid under his bed. He heard his mother attending to his father's wounds. No one came to help him or attend to his wound.

Robby's hole was slow to heal. He had trouble chewing food and favored the non-injured side of his mouth. Weeks passed. When it finally healed, a scar formed. If he smiled, which he seldom did, his siblings laughed at him. They thought he had grown a dimple.

Robby realized he should not utter a sound or reveal his emotions. He never cried. He never talked. To survive, he knew he had to stay inward, that by doing so, he would remain safe. So, he did his best to make himself disappear, if only in his actions.

But once they arrived at the Nova Scotia farm, Robby found a safety net in Uncle Irving, who openly criticized Charles for the way he treated Robby. "He is just a lad. You should not treat him that way. Can't you see that?"

"I will raise my children as I see fit," Charles spat.

"Yes, but the boy should be allowed to play, to talk, to explore." Uncle Irving scooped Robby up in his arms, carried him outside to the farmland stream, and showed Robby the fish. The fast-moving flow bubbled and gurgled as it made its way past them, the fish rocking along the current. He and Uncle Irving continued along the river. They trampled tall grasses and hunted for snakes and salamanders and chased after rabbits. They peered at the birds soaring above the abundant, lush land.

Robby relished the fun he had exploring the farmland with his uncle, but when they returned to the house, a heated exchange ensued between his father and his uncle. Robby did not hear the words. He just heard the anger in his father's voice and the frustration in his uncle's response. Robby braced himself, pushing himself against the wall. His father angrily packed up their belongings, gathered up his wife and children, and pushed them out the door. He denied his bewildered and embarrassed son, Robby, entrance into the car. Once his mom and dad, his older siblings, Terry, Nancy, and Darin, were all seated, his father got behind the driver's seat and, without even a glance at Robby, drove away. Robby saw the shock on his mother's face as she watched Robby from the front passenger window.

As soon as they were gone, Robby was safe. He went inside the small farmhouse and collapsed on the chair. The fear and anxiety he carried with him drained out of him.

Uncle Irving came to his side and wrapped his large hand around Robby's shoulder, and squeezed it. "You'll stay here with us, Bobby-boy."

Aunt May and Uncle Irving made every effort to provide a safe and loving environment for Robby to grow and thrive. Robby loved the farm. He loved Barney, the massive white horse, the cows, the pigs, the hens, and all the wild animals that roamed the land just beyond the barbed-wired fence. He was free to explore the farm and play, given plenty of food, and was never worried about getting slapped or hurt by his uncle and aunt. He placed worms on the fence for the sparrows to eat and was delighted when they ate them. Even better was the moment a sparrow ate a worm out of his hand. He believed at that moment he had made his first devoted friend on the farm. The cool wind made his cheeks blister pink and shook the tree leaves, enticing him to climb them. The giant hawks followed him as he freely ran along the long grasses, weaving in and out of the maple and pine trees, the wild bushes, and the little wildflowers that dotted the ground. With each breath of free air and each step along the land, Robby discarded his pale, bruised skin and grew robust and healthy. His legs no longer hurt him. He was strong, capable, and energetic. He was not the skinny, clumsy kid of his family's east Riverside, Rhode Island home. He spent hours sitting in trees, studying the birds, and learning their behavior, listening to the songs the shaking leaves made in the changing wind speed, surging to loud wrestling, and then dying down to a whisper. He identified each of the birds by their colors, beaks, and tails. He watched the squirrels as they foraged for food. He loved the wind that gently touched him, the cool day's air that made his nose slightly drippy. He loved his Aunt May and Uncle Irving, who kept him by their side as they did their daily work. He helped his uncle clean the barn, stack the hay, feed the chickens, and milk the cows. He watched Uncle make his own horseshoes by welding metal into a perfect form and then mounting them onto his white horse, Barney. Aunt May sewed Robby farm clothes that had all their buttons. Although made of plain material, they shone like brilliant costumes on the newfound boy.

Behind the house, Aunt May and Uncle Irving owned a store. In it, they sold their extra chicken eggs and homemade jars of preserves. She sold feed-hay, the extra cows' milk, and homemade butter. People traded goods too. In exchange for a bale of hay, Irving would accept 65 pounds of fish. Robby helped his aunt manage the store. He attended to the customers, exchanging the goods for money or whatever the buyer had to barter. Robby carried the items to the purchaser's wagon and loaded them on it. On other days, Robby helped Aunt May can the fruits and vegetables to save for the winter months. They carried the jars, fish, other meats, potatoes, carrots, and apples outside to the door in the ground that opened the root cellar. Aunt May jumped inside the four-foot-deep cellar that sunk just to the ground's frost line, and Robby passed her the items that she lay on the chunks of ice Uncle Irving had carved out from the frozen winter river.

Robby became Uncle Irving's shadow. In a gesture of affection, Uncle lifted Robby onto his shoulder and lovingly walked him around the farm, teaching Robby to sing like the birds, croak like the frogs, and find hidden bugs. Robby ran his hand through Uncle Irving's thick gray hair and gazed

down at his uncle's slightly bent nose. His hands were big
and powerful, but his touch was gentle and kind. When
Robby looked into his uncle's eyes, he saw love and trust in
them.

One day while Robby explored the land, winding in
and out of the brush, pushing the grass apart with his feet,
Uncle Irving galloped up to him, perched on the beautiful,
white horse. He reached his massive hand down to Robby,
scooped him up, and placed Robby bareback on Barney.

"Hold onto the mane," he told the lad.

Robby held tight onto the long white threads,
bouncing on the white horse that seemed more mystical and
magical than real. He wondered if the horse would sprout
wings and fly. But feeling the horse's thick muscles rolling
beneath him, his own body lifting and falling with each step
the horse took, Robby knew this horse was purely grounded
on the earth beneath him. A pleasant sensation settled inside
him. He felt as free and wild as the horse's wide gallops. The
rushing wind cleansed Robby and restored his spirit. As they
flew along, Uncle Irving's arm protectively around his waist,
Barney's hooves rhythmically pounded through the brush,
the land stretched forever like Robby's own private heaven
on earth. Here he knew he would survive. Here he began to
formulate the idea that he would not let his father break him.
He would never give in. He was Robby, the prince of this
great Nova Scotia land.

At the farmhouse, Robby slept on a bed, was fed a big
breakfast of bread and butter, eggs, bacon, and grits, and was
allowed to spend the day with Aunt May in the kitchen,
watching her make shepherd pies and apple pies. She taught
him all her recipe secrets as Robby stirred the stews in the

pot. Afterward, Robby sat at the kitchen table and showed her how he had learned to draw with the pencils and sketchpad his sister, Terry, had given him. Robby could not read, but he could draw people with faces, birds with beaks and massive wings, and replicate bugs that he sometimes saw crawling on the ground. In the three months, he stayed on the farm, he transformed into a normal boy with smooth, white skin, piercing blue eyes, a sweet button nose, and thick, brown hair. Uncle Irving, as tall as a giant in Robby's eyes, made Aunt May look smaller but equally resilient when she stood next to him. As a married team, they were Robby's saviors.

Before the rainy season started, Uncle Irving cut the hay and dried it, and then rolled it into bales. He put the bales on the wagon, and Barney pulled them to the barn. The summer was ending. The days grew cooler, the wind fiercer. The planting fields, already harvested, lay bare and waiting for the first winter's frost. The long, wild grasses turned brown. The tree leaves rattled in the wind as if protesting their inevitable loosening from the branches and being swept away in the wind and falling to the ground, where they would become the ground's nourishment. The pungent, sweet smell of the vegetation disappeared as the land settled into its winter slumber.

The day Robby's father and mother came to pick him up to bring him back to their Rhode Island house, Robby wandered around his aunt and uncle's house, agitated and anxious, while his parents visited with his aunt and uncle. Robby went upstairs into the bedroom that was seldom used. Inside the room were three small beds, each covered with homemade, colorful quilts. A small dresser sat against the wall. Aunt May kept a candle continuously lit on a small table next to the window. Every day, she checked the candle. When it was low, she went to the small closet and took out a new candle. She lovingly lit another one to put on top of a plate and then placed it next to the window. Robby knew his aunt and uncle's three sons had been killed in the Canadian-British war. His mother had privately told him that Aunt May and Uncle Irving had watched their three sons walk away to war and never saw them again. One of their sons had become a war-pilot and was killed when he crashed his airplane. The other two had died in war-battles. Aunt May kept a continuous candle lit in their bedroom window, so if her sons ever decided to come home, alive or as ghosts, the lit candle would guide them back to where they belonged.

Robby stood by the window, looking out at the farm. He did not want to leave and go back to East Riverside. He stood brooding, looking out at the land he had grown to love, basking in the tenderness his aunt and Uncle had daily bestowed upon him. They had given him abundant food and loving guidance. As he stared out the window, a wave of sadness washed over him. He wished he did not have to feel so sad all the time. Then, an overwhelming feeling of anger gripped him. He blew out the candle. Immediately, he knew he should not have done it. He stood, watching the smoke lift off the candle wick.

After a while, his mother came into the room. She looked at the candle. "Oh, no!"

Aunt May bolted up the stairs and into the room. When she saw the candle was no longer burning, she threw her hand across her mouth and burst into tears. Uncle Irving and Robby's father raced up the stairs.

His father entered the room. "What has he done now?"

Robby's aunt turned to him. "The candle is out. Now my boys cannot find their way home."

"Did you blow it out?" Robby's father approached his son.

Robby backed up until he hit the wall. He braced himself. "I didn't mean to."

His father swung his right hand and slapped Robby's face. Robby's head jerked to its side and slammed into the wall. His cheek and mouth stung. His nose bled. He turned away. Then he folded forward and wrapped his arms around his waist. He could not stop the tears. Before he knew it, he was sobbing. "I didn't mean to." He wiped his face.

Aunt May hurried to him and closed him in at her waist. She wrapped her arms around him. "It is ok, Bobby-boy. I know you did not mean to do it."

Robby wanted to tell her not to send him home, to keep him there with her, but he could not get his words out. He looked at his uncle, who suddenly looked grieved and sad.

His uncle turned to his dad. "It is such a gift to have a son. To treat him like that… is plain wrong. You are so lucky to have a son like Bobby-boy. You do not appreciate what you have." He shook his head. He always looked a little sad, but now he looked completely disgusted. He reached for Robby, grabbed his hand, and led him downstairs. "Come on, Bobby-boy. Sit with me a bit."

Robby went downstairs with his uncle and sat next to him at the dining table. Robby tried to stop crying, but it took a lot of effort to finally stop the tears from puddling up in his eyes. His uncle gave him a glass of milk and some of Aunt May's homemade bread. Robby stared at the bread for a while.

"Eat up," his uncle said. "You have a long trip home. Best to leave with a full stomach."

Robby bit into the bread. His father came back into the room. Robby turned his back to him. He followed his uncle's advice and ate the food. But no number of treats or kindness could shake the feeling of doom that was settling inside him. His mouth hurt when he chewed the bread. His swollen lip could not close around the glass as he drank the milk. But he managed to put on a brave front for his uncle.

Later that day, the family packed up and drove back to East Riverside, Rhode Island. Robby returned to uncertainty, but in Nova Scotia, under his uncle's care, he had discovered something about himself. He was an explorer of the great Nova Scotia land once settled by the Vikings, who were, in fact, his ancestors.

CHAPTER 3

Robby sat at the kitchen table, thumbing through his button box. It was filled with trinkets his mother had thrown into an old Christmas tin box - zippo cigarette lighter parts, springs and clips, parts of pens, screws, nuts, small brackets, hooks, pieces of wire, pipe cleaners, matches, string, and was kept in a cabinet in the kitchen. It was the only thing Robby was allowed to play with in the house. His mother used the box to keep him quiet at the kitchen table. He picked up parts of old pens and worked on making his own pen.

Completely engrossed in his work, his back to his mother and Nancy as they worked inside the kitchen making dinner for the family, Robby steadily crafted his pen. Robby listened to the shuffle his mother and sister's feet made as they walked on the red and brown linoleum floor. He heard them opening the Pickwick design, knotty pine cabinet doors to pull out ingredients. His Father had hand-crafted the natural pine cabinets, the same ones he custom-made for his customers in his basement wood shop on the weekends for extra money. Except for his mother and Nancy's movements, as they opened and closed the cabinet doors and the sound of his mother's deep breaths as she kneaded the bread dough on the countertop, the house was silent.

Robby sat as quietly as he could at the table, trying to be invisible. Just seven years old, he had recently become aware that his siblings were not being abused in the same manner he was. They were not denied basic food or sentenced to stay in their bedroom for weeks at a time. He noticed none of his classmates were being hit and injured by their fathers. He wondered why he was. He thought he was a bad kid and deserved it, but then he had hardly ever done anything that was worse than what his classmates did or what his siblings did. They were allowed to make as many mistakes as they wanted. They were given abundant food and adequate clothing. He saw other children playing freely and making little mistakes that were overlooked by the grownups. Why was he the only one getting punished?

"You're never going to amount to anything," his father told him over and over. "I am wasting my time on you. You are never going to be a man."

Instinctually, Robby knew his survival depended on how quiet and small he could be, especially when he was inside his house. His coveted button box was the only toy he had ever had. Its contents kept him quiet in the house and out of harm's way most of the time. Daily, he created metal figures, movable gadgets, funny-looking cars, and anything he could dream up to escape the awful truth he was beginning to face – that his father singled him out for mistreatment. For a year now, Robby had not talked much, at least not when his father was home, and his father was home now, sitting in the other room. One sister and his brother were in their bedrooms, their doors shut, but Robby's only refuge was inside his mind. He could live inside his mind, where he could create his own little world and imagine a wonderful life that he lived. He could create amazing things from nothing but scraps in the button box. He became completely absorbed in his work, connecting the pen together, inserting the ink cartridge, screwing it together until the ink-tip poked out, and then clicking it open and shut.

Just the click of the pen stirred his father's anger. He marched into the room, reached the back of his hand at Robby's head, and smacked him so hard his face forward into the button box. Robby lay dazed, unable to move, the contents of the button box scattered on the floor.

Nancy shrieked. She immediately ran to Robby and looked at him. "Robby!"

His mother dropped her knife, released her hand from the raw chicken she was cutting into pieces, and hurried to Robby.

Robby's face pulsated with pain. Nancy lifted his head and touched his face. She looked horrified. His mother's face looked worse. Tears stung her eyes.

Nancy balled her fists at her side. Only four years older than Robby, she was already a tiny, formidable challenger to the abuse her father inflicted on her beloved brother. "Father, if you keep threatening and hurting Robby, he will not survive. Is that what you want for your son?" Her voice elevated into an angry pitch. She fiercely glared at her father.

Their father left the room. Nancy looked at Robby. His mother put her hand to her chest and gasped deep breaths. Nancy wiped the blood from Robby's nose and mouth. She hugged him, holding him close to her. Finally, she released him and wiped the tears from his cheeks. Then she leaned down and carefully put all the scattered miscellaneous items sprawled on the floor back into the button box. When she was finished, she put the button box back into the kitchen cabinet and then helped Robby to the bedroom. She laid Robby down on the bed he shared with his brother. Darin, their brother, ran from the room to be with his father in the living room.

"Dad does this to you because you are smart. You are a genius," Nancy whispered to Robby. "Do not worry now." She wrapped him under a blanket and left the room. Robby was left to recover on his own.

Over the next few weeks, Robby and Darin continuously quarreled in their bedroom. They shared the same double bed. At night, Darin slept with his head near the headboard while Robby's head was at the end of the bed. Before they fell asleep at night, Darin placed his feet in Robby's face. Darin liked to kick Robby in the night, waking Robby up. He often pushed him out of the bed onto the floor.

The boys' nighttime squabbles annoyed their father. Robby, wanting protection, ran to his father to tell him that Darin was hurting him.

"Stop tattling on your brother," his father said, obviously annoyed by Robby's complaint. "I do not want to hear it. If you keep it up, I will separate you both."

One day his father carried a small mattress up the stairs and into the attic. As Robby played in his button box in the kitchen, he listened to his father pull the mattress along the attic floor and then drop it with a loud boom onto the floor. Robby went rigid with fear. The sound of his father's footsteps sent shivers throughout him. His father came down the stairs and stood by Robby. "Since you and Darin cannot get along, you will have to sleep in the attic. Now get on up there."

Robby scurried past his father and ran up the narrow steps. At the end of the stairway, he peeked in through the doorway into the attic space. It was cold, dark, and small. He went inside. The angled ceiling stretched so low that his head bumped it when he stood up. He turned and shut the door. He noticed an inside lock on the door. He turned it and locked himself in the room. For the first time, he realized he was completely safe from his father. No one could get inside the attic unless Robby unlocked the door to let them in. He looked at his new surroundings. The floorboards were wobbly. He had to carefully inch along the boards to steady himself. He walked to the mattress and looked at it. It was small and old. There were no sheets or blankets. The only light came through the small window that looked out onto the side yard and street. He sat down on the mattress and stayed there, looking at his new surroundings. He listened to the muted sounds of his family conducting their normal lives on the main floor below him. The evening settled in. Darkness filled the space. He lay curled on the mattress, cradling his knees to his chest to keep his body warm. He dozed on and off. He slept fitfully.

The morning did not come soon enough. He was cold. His hunger consumed all his thoughts. He sat up and looked at the early light coming through the window. Lifting himself off the mattress and standing as tall as the ceiling allowed, he walked to the window. He watched out the corner until he saw his father's truck leave for work. Then he inched along the floorboards to the door, unlatched it, and opened it. Slowly he stepped down the stairs and entered the kitchen. His mother was at the sink. She turned and looked at him. He had never seen her look so sad.

She wiped her hands in her apron. "Come have some breakfast," she said to him. "Sit down." She brought him a bowl of oatmeal and an entire orange. He ate quickly, working to quell the ache in his belly. He had always been a little hungry, but this painful ache in the pit of his stomach was something new. He hoped he never had to feel this way again.

Over the next few weeks, Robby's father installed a toilet and a sink in the attic, which allowed him to ban Robby up there for days at a time. Most afternoons, while his father was away at work, Robby ventured into the kitchen to be with his mother while she cooked the evening meal. He sat at the table and played with the metal scraps in his button box, bending wire to make animals and piecing together abstract art pieces. Feeling safe with his father gone, he could quietly play. His mother was less tense too. At every chance, while her husband was safely away at work, his mother took out her Mario Lanza albums and played them on the turntable, singing along in perfect unison.

When his mother saw his father's truck pulling into the driveway, she said, "Quick, Robby! Put the record and record player away."

Robby sprang to the record player, carefully lifted the needle off the record, grabbed the record, unplugged the record player, and quickly carried them to the closet in his sister's room. Then Robby ran to the attic, where he shivered in the cold and had no light and listened to his family movement downstairs as they ate dinner together and then settled in for the evening. His mother had given him a warm blanket, but it did not adequately keep him warm.

The hunger Robby felt the first night he spent in the attic continued to grip him. He was often invited to eat dinner with the family, but while the family ate steak, he was given a liverwurst sandwich. At the end of the dinner, Robby was given everyone's potato skins. His father deliberately made Robby eat the leftovers on the plates. He was made to eat the leftover liver and peas his siblings did not eat. After a while, Robby refused to eat it. He sat perfectly quietly. Then he would get up and go into the attic.

At school, the teachers asked his mother why Robby limped around. "And why is he so thin?"

"Oh, he had rickets when he was younger," his mother said. "But he's getting better now."

Robby wondered what the rickets were. How did he get those?

One day Robby sat at the kitchen table and twisted the wires in his button box to make a deer. Manipulating the wires was the only way he could distract himself from knowing his father was in the other room. Quietly, he worked, his ears piqued by the sound of his father stepping into the kitchen. All pretenses to pass as a civil, loving family were dropped when no company was around to witness them all together. Tension filled the air, seeped into every room, and slithered like a venomous snake around the floor. His siblings were in their bedrooms, studying. Only the sound of his mother slicing vegetables on the cutting board and then running water in the sink broke the silence. To better hide Robby's injuries, his father now used rolled-up newspapers for weapons. This resulted in fewer bruises and broken bones for Robby, but the physical effects and emotional toll were becoming evident, even to his sisters.

One day after dinner, Robby, Darin, and Nancy sat at the kitchen table talking. Their mother worked in the kitchen cleaning up after their evening meal. Their father sat in his chair in the living room, reading the paper. The three young siblings took turns making funny faces. They burst into laughter. Robby's chair was against the wall. He leaned back and freely giggled along with his two siblings.

Their father marched into the room. Robby glanced at his father and saw he was annoyed. The three children immediately stopped laughing. Their father's entire face contorted into anger. He pinched his eyebrows, widened his eyes, and flared his nose. He looked at Robby. "If you have enough time to laugh, you aren't busy enough."

Robby had no time to react. His father swung his arm and violently backhanded Robby in the face. The strike was so forceful that Robby's entire head shot through the wall, breaking a huge hole into it. He seized in pain.

His father looked at Robby's head stuck into the wall. "Look what you did! If you had not laughed, there would not be a hole in the wall."

Nancy and Darin got up, pushed their chairs away, and dashed out of the room. Their father stormed off to the living room, dropped onto his chair, and picked up the newspaper. Robby's mom ran to him and eased his head out of the wall. Robby was too stunned to react. Blood oozed from his mouth. Even his teeth hurt. His face immediately began swelling. His mother got some ice from the freezer, wrapped it in a washcloth, and pressed it to Robby's face. Then she helped him stand and walked him to the attic steps. She gave him a push. Robby staggered up the steps. Once in the attic, he locked the door. He went to his mattress and lay down. For a long time, he cradled his throbbing head. The ice did nothing to ease the pain and swelling. He set his nose straight. Only time would heal the injury. And in the attic, time was all he had.

CHAPTER 4

Nancy persisted in her criticism of her Father. After another strong punch to Robby's head, she flew into a rage. "You have to stop this," she said to their father.

Her words stung Robby more than the punch, but he did not flinch or speak. Tears collected in his eyes. He fought to contain them. Even at his youthful age, he knew he could not have his father regard him as weak, so he took a deep breath and stopped the tears before they could escape down his cheeks.

"I'm knocking some sense into him." His father stormed out of the kitchen, leaving Nancy and his mother to tend to his injury.

At school, Robby cried a lot. At recess, the teachers noticed he sat on a ledge by the entrance by himself.

Mrs. Hanson, his teacher, came to his side. "What's the matter, Robby?"

He shook his head. He did not want to talk.

"Is something bothering you?" Mrs. Hanson put her hand on his shoulder and lightly squeezed it.

Robby remained quiet, but tears suddenly flowed like a faucet down his cheeks.

"If you ever have anything you need, you can come to me," she said.

But Robby sat rigid, as still as he could, trying to stop the flow of tears.

"I mean it, Robby." She let go of him. She looked at him for a long time. Finally, she walked away.

At the end of the day, all the kids gathered their books and jackets and left school for the day, laughing and running out the door. But Robby did not leave with them. He sat still at his desk. He kept his head down.

Mrs. Hanson went to him. "Aren't you going to go home?"

"Please don't send me home." Robby began profusely crying, choking back sobs. He wiped his face.

"Why don't you want to go home," she asked.

Robby could not say that he was terrified of his father, that he lived in fear of him, that the very sound of his footsteps sent panic and fear racing inside him.

Mrs. Hanson patted Robby's shoulder. She left the room. Robby sat still at his desk. After a while, the principal, Mr. Bush, came into the room.

He went to Robby and leaned down. "I hear you don't want to go home."

Robby put his elbows on his desk, placed his fists into his eyes, and shook his head.

"Can you tell me why?" Mr. Bush asked.

Robby shook his head. He felt tremendously uncomfortable with the attention he was receiving. He only wanted to sit at his desk. He did not want to go home. But suddenly, he knew that this strategy may not work for him. He needed to leave. With his teacher and the school principal hovering over him, he quietly stood and left the classroom.

But the next day, he refused to go home again. Long after everyone left, he sat crying at his desk. "Please don't make me go home," he begged Mrs. Hanson.

She comforted him with a hug, then gave him a piece of paper and some crayons. "You can draw something while I do my work. You can stay."

Mrs. Hanson walked to her desk and sat down. She quietly worked. Robby began drawing. He drew birds and trees and frogs and other animals. For two hours, he drew detailed pictures of his Uncle Irving and Aunt May's farm. Finally, the day was over. Mrs. Hanson stood and picked up her purse. Robby put the crayons down. He stood. He followed her out of the classroom, down the hallway, and out the door. He did not say goodbye. He was crying too much for that. Slowly, he walked home.

The school called his mother and father in for a conference to talk about Robby's behavior. Robby did not attend, and he did not learn what happened at the meeting. But he could guess. He suspected his father had bullied the teacher and berated the school for not doing their job correctly. Nothing helpful was accomplished. At the end of each school day, he told Mrs. Hanson that he would rather not go home. She kept him with her in the room for as long as she could. Then he left, heading toward home, feeling like a dead child walking to the gallows.

Over time, his mom, Nancy, and Terry came to Robby's aid in other ways. After school, while his father was still at work, his mom made Robby cookies, poured him a glass of milk, and sat with him at the kitchen table. While Robby quietly played with the contents of the button box, she talked to him about what he was making. Every day, she added items to the button box – springs, tiny toy wheels, metal pieces, and, best of all, the little plastic pieces she picked up off the floor at the plastic plant where she worked that looked like moon men. Robby loved those little deformed chunks of rubbery plastic. Using markers, he added button eyes and mouths. On weekend days, when

Robby's father was not going to be home for the day, his mother ran to the corner store, bought Robby a fishing rod, and sent him out for the day to go fishing with his friends at the neighborhood pond.

Terry, the oldest sibling, a teenager, helped Robby by taking him along with her when she spent time together with her friends. Robby was taken to local concerts, to her different friends' houses, and to the local hamburger restaurants. All her friends liked Robby and nicknamed him Little Man.

Nancy was loving and supportive too. When she was out and found discarded toy cars, she pocketed them and brought them home to Robby and put them in his button box. "Remember, Robby," she whispered to him while he worked. "You are a genius."

Robby wondered what a genius he was. His father told him he was stupid, that he would never amount to anything, and that he even deserved to be eliminated.

Every day after school, Robby cringed when he heard his father's car pulling into the driveway. Immediately, he bolted into the basement. He was keenly aware of his father turning the knob at the kitchen door, opening the door, and shutting it. Looking at the ceiling, Robby followed the sound of his father's creaking footsteps into the bathroom, listened to the sound of the toilet flushing, then the sound of his footsteps as he made his way into the living room to his favorite chair. He heard the creaking of the springs as he sank into his recliner, the wrestling of his newspaper, and his mother's steps as she brought him his evening cocktail. Fear gripped Robby. He trembled. He knew what to do to avoid his father's angry outbursts. He stayed there and counted the fifteen minutes. When his father got up, Robby listened to his father walk to the table. Then Robby climbed the stairs, walked to the table, and sat down with the family. His father sat at the head of the table. Everyone was completely silent while they were served the evening dinner.

"Robby doesn't like the dinner," his father said. "Don't give him any." And then he carefully sliced his portion of the chicken and put it in his mouth, savoring the taste with a contented sigh. Robby's four siblings ate quietly, gently placing their utensils down by their plates to keep the sound-level down.

Robby sat staring at the wall while his parents and siblings ate a robust dinner.

One by one, his siblings recited to their father how their school-day went, but instead of an enthusiastic rundown, they each gave a strict account of what they had learned in each classroom and what grade they had received that day in their homework assignments. Their father expected /A/s and settled for nothing less. Robby was excluded from the conversation and not invited to give an account of his day.

When dinner was finished, his mother brought out her homemade apple pie. She gave each family member a slice of the pie. But when she tried to give Robby one, his father shook his head.

"Robby hates apple pie, so he won't have a slice," he said.

"But, dad," Nancy protested. "Robby loves pie."

"If I give him a slice of it, then there won't be a left-over piece for me later," their father said.

"But, dad," Nancy insisted.

"The only pie that Robby likes is lemon meringue. That is the only pie Robby will eat," their father said.

Darin and Terry took bites of their pie. Their mother went to the refrigerator. She came back with a special slice of lemon meringue pie she had earlier made to give Robby when her husband denied her son dessert. She put the slice in front of Robby. He looked up at her. She winked at him. Robby loved lemon meringue pie and was thrilled to be given a piece of it. He slowly ate it, pretending he did not like it.

When the family had finished eating their dessert, Robby's father looked at him. "You do the dishes."

"Robby hates to dry the dishes most of all," Nancy said. "How about I wash them, and Robby be made to dry them."

"Fine." Their father wiped his mouth with his napkin, dropped it onto his plate, stood, and retreated to the living room to finish reading the paper.

Nancy and Robby cleared the table. They stood by the kitchen sink. Nancy filled the sink with water and dishwashing soap. She reached into her pocket and gave Robby a small car. He took it and ran it across the patterned kitchen counter while Nancy washed the dishes.

"Look at this, Robby." She scooped up the dishwater suds and made a soapsuds' mustache and beard on her face for him to see. "You try it."

Robby made a bubble mustache and beard on his face. He looked at Nancy and smiled.

Nancy continued to play with the bubbles. "Look, you can make mountain peaks." She sunk her hand into the sink water and brought it up over and over until the sink was full of soapy-bubble mountain peaks. When he looked at her, he felt overwhelmed with love. Nancy allowed Robby to eat all the leftover dinner food, feeding him bites of it before they washed each dish. Then, when they were done playing and doing the dishes, Robby went back to his attic, hidden away, invisible again.

CHAPTER 5

Winter settled in, confining everyone to the house after school. The attic was cold. At night, Robby lay under his meager blanket. The window cast the dim moonlight inside and allowed Robby to see his breath escape from his mouth and disperse into the frigid air. The wintry air became another enemy he battled to survive. On other days, while his father was working at the chemical plant, Robby quietly sat at the kitchen table and played with the scraps and gadgets in his button box. The school brought relief from the cold temperatures.

Robby's mom was delighted when Charles decided to take the kids ice skating at the local pond. She was busy with household chores, and an empty, quiet house would give her a break from her children for a while. She cheerfully went around the house, gathering the children's warm clothes, their hats, mittens, and then the skates.

"Even you're going," she told Robby. "Darin has an old pair of ice skates he has outgrown, so you can use them."

Robby loved the winter outdoor activities. Often, he had walked to the Willett Avenue Pond near the edge of his housing development and had watched the children ice skating on the pond and wished he could try skating too. Now was his chance to show his dad how well he could skate. His dad would be proud of him. His mother dressed him in a jacket, a hat, mittens, denim pants, and socks. Robby walked with his three older siblings and his father to the pond. Once there, they sat on the ground and slipped into their ice skates. The bright sun did not alleviate the bitingly frigid wind, but Robby looked forward to learning to skate. He laced his skates. They were too big for him. His feet slipped around inside of them. He was not deterred. He looked at the numerous families out on the ice and saw they all easily glided along the ice. He thought he would too.

His two sisters held hands and entered the ice. Darin followed. They laughed as they supported each other from falling. Robby tried to stand up. His feet slipped. He fought to keep his balance.

His father hovered over him. "Get on the ice," he told his son.

Nancy turned back and helped Robby onto the ice. Her grip gave Robby some support, but his feet wobbled around inside the skates. His skates slipped right out from under his legs. He fell hard on the ice. His legs bent in different directions. Nancy lifted his arms and helped him to his feet, but he continued slipping around, unable to stand still.

"Let go of him," his father told Nancy.

But she held onto him. If she let go of him, he would fall and not get up. "Come on, Robby."

"Let him go," his father shouted to Nancy.

"I'll get the camera and take a photo of you ice skating," she whispered to him. She squeezed his hand and let go.

Immediately, Robby lost his balance. He fell forward onto his hands and knees.

"Get up," his father shouted.

Robby got up, but he fell again. Pain shot through his legs. His hands and wrists hurt. He shivered. "Daddy!"

"How are you ever going to be a man if you don't learn to get up when you fall," his father said. He leaned down and shouted in Robby's face. "Now get up."

Robby stood, waving his arms to steady himself. He fell. Determined, he pushed himself up again and tried to secure his balance. He fell again. His father demanded. He pulled himself up. His knees bled. The blood seeped through his pants and ran down his legs and onto the skates. The shoelaces were saturated with blood. Robby ignored the pain and kept trying. He focused on the ice and waved his arms to help maintain his balance. He wanted to please his dad and show him that he could skate. But the skates were too big, and his feet slipped all around the inside of them. He repeatedly fell.

The other skaters stopped and watched Robby trying to skate.

"Get up," his father shouted.

"Hey, you, mister," another father said to Charles. "Leave the kid alone. You are hurting him. Can't you see the blood on his pants?"

"He is my kid. I will raise him the way I see fit," his father shouted at the man.

Robby stood again and slipped along, trying to balance himself. Nancy took a photo of him, but instead of looking at the camera to smile, he glanced downward.

Nancy grabbed his arm and walked him off the ice. She helped him to the ground, took off his skates, and put his shoes on. She lifted him up, wedged her arm under his armpit, and walked him home. His legs hurt. Robby limped. When they walked through the back door into the kitchen, a burst of warm air gave him his first relief from the harrowing experience. His mother turned from the kitchen sink and stared at him. A pained expression washed over her face. She dropped the knife in the sink. She hurried to Robby, picked up his little, frozen body, and carried him into the bathroom. She helped him remove his jacket, his hat, and his wet gloves, then gingerly pulled off his soaking socks. She eased him out of his pants. Robby was too exhausted to respond.

"Dad did it, Mom," Nancy said. "He made him skate in those skates that were too big for him. When he fell, Dad yelled at him to get up on his own. Even the other skaters tried to stop Dad." She reached into the medicine cabinet and pulled out some ointment.

His mother washed his knee wounds with a warm, wet washcloth, then wiped the blood that ran down his legs. Robby sat on the stool, feeling too numb and shocked to speak. His mother then applied medicine to his wounds. She cleaned the cuts on the palm of his hands. "You'll be all right." When she was done, she and Nancy carried Robby to Darin's bed and laid him on it.

When his father came home with Terry and Darin, Pearl confronted him. "Why did you hurt Robby like that? You must stop this."

"He must learn to be a man. "

"He's just a little boy," Pearl said.

"He is weak-legged. Can't hardly walk. He will never be normal," his father said.

"You hurt him." Pearl cried. "How could you do that to him?"

"He's not my son, that's why." Charles stormed off into the living room.

For two weeks, Robby lay in bed, unable to move. His knees slowly healed. He developed an upper respiratory infection and ran a high fever. His mother sat with him as often as she could and rubbed Vicks' cream on his chest to soothe him.

His father arrived home with heavy metal leg braces and dropped them on the bed next to Robby. "Since you can't walk right, you can wear these."

Pearl walked into the room. She looked angry. "He's not wearing those."

"He's crippled," his father said.

"Because you hurt him. That is why," Pearl said.

"He's always been that way," Charles said.

"Those are old braces used for polio victims."

"They work," Charles said.

"I refuse to put those on my son." Pearl threw down her dishtowel and stormed out of the room.

Robby looked at the braces. They were made of thick metal and looked heavy and clumsy. If he used them, he knew he would fall flat on his face. But he could walk. If only his father would leave him alone. He lay in bed, grateful for the warm blanket and the comfort his mother gave him.

Finally, he recovered. His physical wounds healed, but something inside him had broken for good. He would not reveal his emotions. He no longer responded to anyone who talked to him, nor would he look at anyone who came near him. Terry encouraged him to draw pictures. She gave him crayons, pencils, pens, and a paper pad. Robby sat at the kitchen table quietly and drew. His mother worked at the kitchen counter, making dinner for the family. She was pregnant with her fifth child and due soon. She stopped working, stood up straight, reached back and pressed her hands to her back to soothe its ache.

Robby took the black pen and opened the book to the first blank page. On the top, open-ended corner, he drew a spider sitting on a ledge. On each of the following pages, he dropped his spider farther and farther downward. On the last page, he drew the spider dead at the bottom with a webbed noose around him. The spider had hung himself. He showed his flipbook to Terry. He held the pad up and quickly flipped through the pages, revealing the spider's downward descent to the final page. When she saw the spider dead at the bottom, she frowned. She patted Robby on his head and walked away. Next, he drew an oak tree with a detailed bark and trunk. Leaves dotted the branches. He surrounded the tree with darkness, coloring the background completely black. In another drawing, he drew an outline of his face. He colored the rest of the page completely black. He sketched the inside of his white face with black eyes. He had no mouth.

Terry took his drawings. A few days later, she burst into the back door. She looked at her mother, who was standing near the kitchen sink, and then at Robby, sitting at the table drawing. He glanced up at her but quickly returned to his drawing.

"Mom," Terry said. "I took Robby's drawings to a psychiatrist to have him look at them. I asked him to give me his opinion of them. He said the artistry was exquisite, but the art showed a deeply troubled person. He said the artist had drawn self-portraits, that he had entered a deep level of introversion, and that he was not behaving within his consciousness. The psychiatrist thought it was a dangerous place for a person to be."

Robby heard what Terry said, but he did not respond. His mother did not respond either, except to wring her hands in her apron.

"You have to do something, Mom," Terry insisted.

Robby stopped listening. He concentrated on making a duck with some wire, twisting it into a perfect replica of the ducks he had seen at the river and streams near his house. When he finished it, he placed it on the table and looked at what he had created. The duck sat flat on the table, the wings at its side, the beak protruding between the eyes.

"He doesn't talk, Mom," Terry continued.

Robby heard his sister's words. She was wrong about him. Of course, he could talk. But he preferred not to. If he talked or even moved, he would no longer be invisible. He would not be safe. It was better to sit completely still, not move his head or show any facial expression and keep his body motionless. His only world became inside his mind. There, hidden from his family, was a door he could open to an entirely new existence. There he found peace. No one else was allowed in. His mind was a place of enlightenment. He envisioned a new world completely different from the one he lived in. In his world, people loved and cared for him. They offered him food, even apple pie with ice cream. His mind was full of color and a lovely, wonderful golden land with a bright blue sky. A river gurgled and meandered in a way that soothed his soul. Trees reached upward to the open sky. Bears and deer roamed freely around him. And always, the white horse was there, the massive muscles pulsating as he galloped freely. The shadow of his uncle Irving stood in the distance, watching over him, keeping him safe until the real world drew him out of his min. Whether with abuse or a morsel of food, Robby had found his inner sanctuary.

Terry stormed out of the kitchen and into her bedroom. Robby's mother brought him some milk and cookies. She sat with him for a minute, looking concerned. Then she stood and continued making dinner.

Robby's teacher, Mrs. Hanson, arrived at the house to talk to his parents.

His father called out. "Robby, come here."

His mother went to the attic entrance, climbed the long stairs to the attic door and called. "Robby! It's your teacher. She has come for a visit. Isn't that nice?" she called through the door.

Robby sat up on his mattress and listened.

"Robby, please come here," his mother called. "Come talk to your teacher."

Robby hesitated.

"Robby!" his father's voice boomed.

He pivoted, placed his feet on the wobbly constructed wood floor and pushed himself to a standing position. His teacher? Here? He walked to the door and opened it. His mother beckoned him to follow her down the stairs. He stepped down behind her and followed her to the front door. Mrs. Hanson stood, her hands clasped in front of her, her purse draped on her bent elbow, and her lips pursed. She turned her eyes to Robby's face and looked intently at him. Mrs. Hanson, one of the oldest teachers at the school, was known for her strictness but also her compassion.

"How are you, Robby?" she asked him, looking concerned.

Robby stood rigid. He did not look at her. He looked well beyond her out into the street at the garbage cans he wanted to go through to find any little treasures that would eventually be useful to him.

His father firmly grasped his shoulder. "He's fine. Aren't you, son?"

Robby did not respond.

His father shook his shoulder. "Don't be rude. Say hello to your teacher."

"Hello," Robby said.

"May we talk in private," Mrs. Hanson said to his father.

"Robby, you are excused," his father said.

The frightened boy turned and walked to the attic door, up the stairs, and back into the attic. He locked himself inside. Although cool outside, he went to the window and quietly cracked it open. He faintly heard his teacher talking to his father. He caught some of the words she said. "Too quiet. Will not move. Will not do any of his work. Concerned. Worried. Never.... seen." Then his mother spoke. "I will.... talk to him.... make sure...."

Robby watched his teacher walk back to her car. Her back to him, he could not see her face, but he saw the way she hurriedly walked as if she too were trying to get away from his father. Robby imagined leaping out the window, flying far away from the attic from the paralyzing fear of his father's horror. As he watched his teacher drive away, he followed her with the wings he had suddenly grown. But then his father's booming voice shouted up the attic's stairwell. "Robert! Right now. Come coco!"

Robby could not move. He had locked the attic from the inside so no one could reach him. If he wanted, he could remain safe inside the attic. But then he wondered what would happen to him if he did. Eventually, he would have to face his father. If he waited, the punishment might be worse. It took all his strength to navigate his way to the door, over the loose floor planks, leaning down so his head did not hit the ceiling beams. When he reached the door, he opened it slowly. The light below cast his father's silhouette across the entrance. In Robby's eyes, it took on the form of a monster about to engulf him. Robby made his way down the creaking stairs, his hands on the enclosed walls to steady himself. He reached the last step and kept his head down.

"When I say, come coco, you come coco," his father shouted. He reached and grabbed Robby's thin shirt and pushed him. He backhanded Robby in the face. The sharp blow snapped Robby's head backward.

Terry, standing nearby, ran from the room. His mother gasped.

"I don't ever, I mean, ever, want to have to answer the front door to your teacher complaining to me how you will not do your work. You hear me?" his father said.

Robby turned around and bolted back up the stairs to the attic. Once inside, he slammed the door and locked it. He was safe for now.

But Mrs. Hanson persisted. During parents' night at the school, when they visited Robby's classroom, the teacher once again approached Robby's parents and reported that Robby was still withdrawn. Robby did not participate in any classroom activities except his art lessons. He drew dead insects at the bottom of his pages. Robby stood nearby, listening to the teacher tell his parents that she was very worried about their son. He did not complete his assignments. Robby wanted to tell them that he could read and do math. But he did not speak up. His mother promised to help Robby. His father remained quiet, but Robby saw he was angry.

Quickly, his parents turned to leave, but the principal approached them. He looked serious. He did not hesitate to talk. "Your son is withdrawn."

Robby's father pushed the principal aside and walked out of the room. Robby and his mom followed. Darin came happily, skipping behind them. Robby was terribly embarrassed and ashamed about his school performance. He had done something terribly wrong. He felt exposed to everyone around him, his parents, his teachers, and the principal, when all he wanted was to be invisible, to be left alone and to not be hurt. Now he had made things worse. In trying to protect himself, he had made his gravest error. He had worsened his prospects for survival. He trudged sluggishly toward the car and stood by the back door, not wanting to get in, knowing that when he was inside, and they were driving home, his father would have the privacy to berate and physically admonish him. His mother opened the door and urged him into the back seat. Feeling defeated, Robby got into the backseat. Darin hopped in next to him on the other side and freely slammed the door. His mom slowly opened the front passenger side and stiffly lowered herself onto the seat. She glanced back at Robby and gave him a slight smile. But her face looked worn and sad. When his father pulled the driver's side door open, she quickly jerked her head forward and stared out the window. His father sat in the driver's seat and started the engine. Robby took a deep breath, almost gasping, and folded his hands in his lap. Even the air seemed to have left the car once his dad got in it. Everyone was silent as his dad drove home. Robby looked out the window. The trees along the road loomed like giants, the leaves shaking in the sudden wind. Robby expected to be beaten when they arrived home. But, when they walked into the house, his mother quickly scooted him up the stairs toward the attic. Robby hurried, got inside the attic, and shut the door. He locked it. He was safe. He lay on his mattress and let the tears flow.

The next day, after school, before his father arrived home from work, his mother sat Robby at the kitchen table and gave him the button box to play with. As he worked on making a little spider out of wire, his mother attentively conversed with him.

"You have amazing mechanical talent," she told him. "You remind me so much of Uncle Irving. He has always been so proud of you."

He pretended he was not listening to his mother. He focused on the task of making a little pulley with a small chain attached to a wheel. Beside him sat a spider he had just finished making out of wire.

"I'll look for more things to add to your box," she said. "I really like your spider."

She went to the refrigerator and got out a carton of milk. She poured it into a large glass all the way to the top, then grabbed a handful of oatmeal cookies from the cookie jar and brought them to Robby. "Here you are, son." She put them on the table and sat next to him. For an hour, she watched Robby work on creating little animals out of screws, bolts, and wires. "I really like your creativity," she told him.

Robby did not look at her or respond. He focused on his little creations. After he made each one, he placed it on the table and moved to the next animal. He made a whale, a raccoon, a rabbit, and a fox. Finally, he ate a cookie and drank some of the milk. His mother smelled like apples and the chicken potpie she had placed in the oven to cook. He loved her smell. He loved hearing her speak kind words. But he could not look at her. He was completely focused on his button box.

His father began bringing home small plastic animals. He walked in the door and put a little blue rabbit or a bird or a cat on the table for Robby. Sometimes his father hid the little animals under the tablecloth for Robby to find. Each time a little plastic animal was left on the table beside him, Robby ignored it and continued inventing things to make from the scraps in the button box. It was better for him to pretend the gifts were not there than to acknowledge them. For a few weeks, his father continued to bring him the little plastic animals, but Robby continued to ignore his father and the plastic animals, figuring if he touched them, he would get smacked in the head.

But Robby's approach backfired on him. His father became impatient. If Robby did not at least find the animal under the tablecloth and pick it up for even just a moment, his father would go into a rage and slap the back of his head, causing him to lurch forward. But Robby would not acknowledge that he liked the little animals and wished he could keep them. As he played in his button box, he snuck glances at the little plastic animals sitting beside him and wished he could touch them. They were the only gifts he had ever received, yet playing with them was too risky. Better to stay deep inside himself, all alone, where he felt safe. But the more animals his father placed next to him, the quieter he became and the sadder he felt. Yet, he longed for those little animals. He wanted them more than anything in the world. He wanted a toy. He wanted to be loved and accepted. But he was not. Daily his father reminded him that he would not amount to anything, that he was incorrigible, a stupid idiot, an unworthy son.

One Friday, his father came home from work, and instead of bringing Robby a little plastic animal, he backhanded him in the back of his head, throwing him against the table. Robby's face slammed into the hard table.

His Father leaned into him. Robby cowered, almost cried out, but he sucked it in. Every muscle in his body, from his head down to his toes, tightened in defiance.

"You did not like what I gave you, so I am going to show you my other side. I tried to be nice. You didn't accept it, so now I am not going to be nice anymore."

Fear pulsated through Robby. He would not reveal his shock.

"Do you hear?" His Father's voice boomed.

Robby froze.

"I brought you into this world and I'm going to take you out," his father said.

His Mother stopped making her dinner casserole. His sisters stopped giggling. Only his brother, Darin, could be heard in the other room giving a slight sound of delight at his brother's suffering. Robby sat up, not daring to touch his facial injury or wipe the blood oozing from his mouth.

"You get six weeks in the attic. Now, get!" his father boomed as if chasing a nasty dog away.

Robby stood and staggered up the stairwell, his tiny frame wobbling back and forth, feeling the swelling in his jaw. When he got to the attic, he shut and locked the door. He dropped to the floor and lay there, physically and emotionally spent. He listened to his father walk up the attic stairs and lock the attic door from the outside, so Robby could not get out. Robby crawled to the mattress and lay on it. The familiar feeling of despair and hopelessness washed over him, filling every pore of his body. Dread engulfed him. He might not ever get out of the attic. He would die there. He began trying to figure out how to escape. He looked around the attic, searching for something, anything that would get him out of his confinement. He would not stand being locked away.

He stood and walked around the attic, looking for a way to escape his prison. The window that opened to the sideyard was small. Even if he could get out of it, he would have to jump a long way to the ground. He could be injured in the fall. He scoured the walls for a hole he could escape through, but the attic was very sound except, he realized, the floorboards. They were not secured tightly to the floor. He got down on his hands and knees and began lifting the loose boards. Underneath them were little areas where he could stash his items if he wanted to. He inched along the floor until he reached the door that led out to the attic stairs. He looked up and saw the lock that he had secured to keep his father out. Once inside the attic, no one could reach him. He looked at the floorboards by the door. He knew they were loose because every time he stepped into the attic, he had to

be careful not to slip on them. He lifted several of them.
There was enough room for him to slip through the hole.
The hole was next to the back side of the stairs. The stairs
had no backing between each step. He looked all the way
down and saw he could slip down the back of the stairs and
reach the cellar. Then all he would have to do is walk across
his father's woodshop to the cellar steps and climb them.
Opening the door, he would be liberated.

 He dropped through the floor and grabbed the stairs.
Slowly, stealthily, he inched his way down the stairs, gripping
the edges of the stairs with his fingers, struggling to hold the
weight of his body, his legs dangling free. When he got to the
cellar floor, he dropped onto the floor. Like lightning, he ran
across the dark cellar to the stairs. He lightly climbed them,
opened the cellar door, and stepped outside. He shut the
door. He was out. Quickly he ran to the back of the yard. He
climbed a willow tree as high as he could. He sat down on a
branch that was hidden from view, straddled his legs on
either side and breathed in the air. The air circled throughout
his body, loosening his arms, his legs, and his very lungs as if
releasing him from the paralysis he endured in the house
with his family. He looked up at the sky, the brilliant sun
now inching its way down to the west. Soon the night would
fall, and he would see the brilliant stars. The branches
swayed, soothing him like a baby in a cradle, the wind
wrestling the leaves as if they were singing nature's chimes
just for him. He leaned against the trunk, his legs dangling
down, and exhaled. He was free.

CHAPTER 6

Robby's mother delivered another baby girl she named Alice. With a new baby and four other children to take care of, his mother was too busy to spend time with Robby after school as he sat in the kitchen playing with the contents of the button box. Often confined to the attic, Robby was beginning to become an invisible family member.

Robby loved the family dog, a beagle named Tammy. His father had installed a backyard kennel to keep the dog fenced in. To escape his father, Robby often went to the backyard to play with her. Tammy could tease and play in a way that delighted Robby. He ran around the yard, chasing her, while she zigzagged around him, circling around the trees, kicking up loose dirt. Tammy's energy was infectious. Robby's pain subsided. His emotions lifted. When they were finished, he gave her some water in her bowl and then curled up beside her in the kennel with his arm around her. Tammy was the one happy part of his childhood.

His father hated Tammy's barking. He complained. "That dog is annoying."

To keep her from barking, Robby spent as much time as he could with her. In the mornings, he ran to the kennel to greet her. But one morning, he found her unresponsive. She lay lifeless, her head resting on her front legs, her tail curled around her body. Robby tried to wake her, but she would not move. He touched her head to wake her, but she remained still. She was dead. Robby was appalled. He ran inside the house crying. He raced to the attic and locked himself inside. How did she die? The day before, she had been eager to play and full of energy. Robby got his pencil and paper and drew a picture of her lying on the ground. The drawing was a perfect replica of his precious dog. He tacked the photo to the wall next to his mattress. Then he lay down and cried until he fell asleep.

The next day, while his father was at work, Robby went downstairs and sat in the living room alone. His mother was in the back bedroom with his baby sister, Alice. His other sisters were doing their homework. Robby saw Alice's stuffed monkey lying on the floor. He picked it up, grabbed its arm, and swung it around and around. As he whipped the little monkey, the anger he carried inside him began to fester and grow. Rage heaved inside him. He stopped swinging it and backhanded the monkey across its face. He flung it down on the floor. Immediately, he knew what he had done was wrong. Robby had mimicked what his father did to him. It did not feel good to hurt someone. It did not feel good at all. He felt ashamed of himself. He never wanted to hurt anyone. If he felt that, his father must feel it too. For the first time, he understood the rage his father must feel when he backhanded him. Now he knew his father was wrong to hit him. Robby had found his defense.

That night when his father backhanded him across the back of his head, Robby stood up to his father. He put his little face next to his dad's face and said, "Does that make you feel good? Does that make you happy to hit me? Go ahead. Hit me again." He opened his eyes wide and stared defiantly at his father.

His father looked unnerved. Robby's words disarmed him. Robby immediately turned and walked away. For the first time, he had gained some leverage, a bit of power over his dad. He had gained some control.

In 3rd grade, Robby's teacher, Mrs. Wollman, clasped her hands together and said to the class. "We are going to have a classroom art competition. Each student will do a poster-size drawing. The winner will be chosen by the students." She handed each student a poster board. "Take out your colored pencils and crayons and use them to draw your art piece."

Robby's favorite subject in school was art. It was the only subject he completely immersed himself in.

"You only have an hour to complete it, so everyone, get to work," she said.

Robby laid his poster board across his desk and used crayons and colored pencils to draw a racetrack. Then he drew several race cars racing along the track. All the cars were upright on the track except one that had flipped over. He used the black pencil to sketch a detailed drawing of the entire underside of that car, and for a special effect, he drew smoke emitting off the car. Each car had its own distinct color, and he drew a race number on the hood of each one.

When the hour was up, Mrs. Wollman said, "Time to stop, class. Print your name on the back of your drawing and place it on the corner table. Tonight, I will hang them up. Tomorrow, you can vote for your favorite drawing."

Robby placed his drawing on the top of the pile and then sat back down. He glanced at some of the other art pieces. Most of the other children had drawn garden scenes with houses and kids playing in the yards. He knew his was the best one. He thought he would win the contest.

The next day when he arrived at his classroom, he looked at all the drawings tacked on the walls, circling the classroom. He sat down at his desk.

Mrs. Wollman said, "You have all created unique and interesting art. I wanted to give you a chance to create a piece completely on your own just to see how varied the artwork would be. I must say, you have created expressions of yourselves, your lives, and your thoughts. That is what a true artist does."

Robby looked at the pieces. Becky had drawn a self-portrait. Sue had drawn trees by a stream. The boys had drawn deer and birds. Some had drawn cars, but no one had drawn an entire race car track of cars racing around it with one that had crashed and turned over. None had thought to draw the underside of the car in detail with the muffler, pipes, and tires burning from the heat.

"Becky, will you please go around and number all the paintings? Then, students, you will vote for your favorite by writing its number down on the piece of paper I will give you. That will make the judging impartial to bias. You will not be able to vote for your best friend's painting."

Becky walked to each painting and wrote the numbers on them, starting with one and continuing up. Robby watched her write a large 7 in the corner of his painting. He was mortified. The glaring black seven desecrated his masterpiece. His painting was ruined. She had ruined it. It was not fit for the show anymore. He no longer wanted to participate in it. No one should write on someone's art piece. That was not fair. It was not right.

Calmly, he walked over to his teacher's art cabinet, opened it, and took out a bottle of black paint and a sponge. He took them to the classroom sink and poured the paint on the sponge. Then he carried the sponge to his race car drawing and brushed black paint all over his piece until it was nothing but a wall of black paint. The only remaining visible portion was the number seven. Then he rinsed the sponge in the sink and put the paint and sponge back in the cabinet. He sat down.

Mrs. Wollman looked at Robby. She seemed completely surprised by his behavior. He looked back at her. He sat politely. She did not speak to him. She continued with the day. Robby was no longer interested in learning anything that day, but he sat quietly and pretended to be listening.

Mrs. Wollman passed out a piece of paper for them to cast their vote, but she skipped Robby. "Students, I want you to pick the painting you want to win. Write the painting's number on your paper, fold it, and put it in the drawing box on my desk. You may begin now." She walked to her desk and sat down. Then she looked at Robby. "Please come here."

Robby stood and walked over to her. He waited to see what she was going to say.

"Since you eliminated your painting from the contest, I want you to go to my cabinet, get out the towels and cleaning solution, and go to all the sinks in the school and clean them. I wish I didn't have to eliminate your vote, but this is your detention."

Robby did not show any emotion. He was an expert at that. He pivoted and walked to the cabinet, got the cleaning supplies, and left the room. He cleaned all the classroom sinks, all the hall sinks, and all the bathroom sinks. If he had to clean the sinks, he would do an excellent job. He worked the rest of the day. He left the cleaning supplies at his classroom door and ran out of school.

Every day after Robby returned home from school, he did not venture around the house but stayed close to the kitchen while his mother cooked. He focused on the contents of the button box and created his little creatures and mechanical items.

When his father came home from work on Friday, he said to Robby. "I'm going to give you a chance to prove you are a man. If you clean my woodshop tomorrow, I will let you go fishing with your friends in the afternoon."

Robby's interest piqued. Could it be real? Would he have a day to go fishing with his friends?

"For now, you can spend the rest of the day in the attic." His father went into the cellar to do his work. Robby quickly disappeared into the attic. He listened to the family eating supper together at the kitchen table, heard his father's booming voice demanding each child give him an explanation about what they learned in school, the timid voices of his sisters, and the cocky way his brother responded. Darin was the golden boy who not only looked like his father with the same eye color, protruding ears, barrel chest, and chin but acted like his father too. His mother did not make a sound for the entire meal.

Robby's siblings never got hit and never had to fear their father. Only Robby had been singled out. Robby had lost his place within the family. Instinctively, he knew he did not belong in the house. He never would belong there. His Father had beaten it in him that he would never amount to anything in life.

But in the attic, he lay under his blanket on the mattress and dreamed he was somewhere else. Mostly, he thought about his Uncle Irving and Aunt May's home in

Nova Scotia. He had spent three summers there already and knew he belonged with them. They loved him. He loved being inside their house, snug in the layered shirts his aunt gave him to wear. With them, he was free to roam the countryside. He had grown to love the howling, cool Canadian wind. He climbed trees and studied the birds, named them, and watched the way they gathered seeds and made their nests. He learned to whistle like a bird. Safe in the tree, he watched the bears roam the land and the deer eat the brush and grass. At dusk, owls flew by him, their giant wings soaring across the land. Stars blanketed the sky in a display of twinkling, brilliant light. Shooting stars bolted down the sky. Robby belonged there, in nature, in the wild, where no one could hurt him. Under the blanket in the dark attic, Robby could manage his sadness by imagining that he was in a large maple tree in Nova Scotia on that great land, where he was free and welcomed.

The next morning Robby's father promised him if he cleaned the wood shop, he would be allowed to go fishing with his friends. Robby quickly called his neighborhood friends and told them to come by in the early afternoon to go fishing with him. Cheerfully, he began cleaning his father's woodshop. While he wiped the machinery, organized the wood in stacks along a wall and swept the floor, he imagined going to Echo Lake with his friends, casting his line in the water while he sat with them, eating peanut butter and jelly sandwiches together, passing a jug of juice around. He imagined they would catch so many fish that they would have to throw most of them back, but they would save some to take home to their families. Oh, the joy of having a day with his school friends, just to have fun and laugh.

But when Robby finished the job, his father came into the cellar. "Take the barrels out to the trash." He left Robby alone to do the final task.

The barrels were full to the top with chipped wood and sawdust and miscellaneous items his father had thrown away. Robby pushed them to the cellar steps, but the barrels were so heavy he could not lift them up the steps. After an hour of trying, he finally gave up. This was a task he simply was not strong enough to do. Surely his father would see that. Robby gave up and got ready to go fishing with his friends. He made peanut butter and jelly sandwiches, poured the juice into a jug, closed the top, got his fishing pole from the garage, and placed all his belongings outside against the side of the house. Then he went into the attic to get dressed to go.

Finally, his friends walked over to his house to pick Robby up for the long walk to Echo Lake. He was finally having an adventure. He hurried to his friends to greet them. "Hello!" he cheerfully said to Paul, Tommy, and Willie. He ran to scoop up the lunches he had prepared for his friends.

But suddenly, Robby's father charged out of the house. Robby looked at him and saw he was irate. Fear shot like an electric bolt from Robby's feet up to his neck. His heart furiously beat.

His Father ran up to his son. "Why didn't you do what I told you to do?"

From his father's angry expression and the heaving of his breath, Robby knew he was in deep trouble. "I did," he said, sticking up for himself around his friends. "I did."

"I told you to clean the cellar. You did not get the barrels to the trash." His Father took Robby's arm and shook it.

Robby fought back tears. "I couldn't lift them up the steps. They were too full."

"Get in the attic. You are not going fishing today." His Father shook his arm so violently Robby's entire body wobbled. He struggled to remain standing. Mortified, he could not look at his friends. His eyes blurred.

Willie, the boy down the street, shouted at Robby's Father. "You are not a nice man. You're mean to Robby."

A tear ran down Robby's cheek. Even at his youthful age, he knew his father never had any intention of letting him go fishing with his friends. He had set Robby up to fail. Tommy picked up a rock and threw it at his father. It landed two feet away from him. His father let go of Robby and waved his hand at his friends. "Scat! Get out of my yard and do not come back." Then he grabbed Robby's shirt collar and dragged him into the house, through the living room, the kitchen, and to the attic stairs. "Two more weeks in the attic. You can try to do a better job cleaning the cellar next week." He pushed Robby. The humiliated boy ran up the stairs, through the door, and slammed it shut. He turned the lock. He was left alone.

Robby lay down on the floor. He was gripped with a jumble of humiliation, hurt, and anger. He realized that as long as he lived in the house with his father, he would never have a life. Despair filled him. In the dark room, Robby felt his spirit leave his body. Everything ceased to exist. Inside he was like an empty shell as if the darkness in the attic had climbed inside him and erased him. He felt himself leave his body and hover over it. The plug on his vessel had been pulled, and he had leaked out of it. But then something happened. He cried. His tears let him know that he was indeed inside his body. And he was still alive, if only just an inner tiny flame that struggled to stay ignited. He lay crumpled, staring at the darkness, slowly breathing until merciful sleep released him.

Two weeks later, his father told Robby and Darin that he would buy them bikes if they cleaned the cellar. Robby wanted to believe his father would buy him a new bike. If he did an excellent job cleaning, he would finally get something to call his own. And this time, he would have his brother's help getting the barrels up the cellar steps and into the bins.

On the floor, underneath the wood saws, sawdust was two inches deep. Robby started sweeping the floor. Darin snuck up behind Robby and hit him on the top of his head with the end of a hammer, not hard enough to crack his head open but hard enough to cause swelling. Robby darted away from him. He continued sweeping. Instead of helping to clean, Darin swung the hammer around in a threatening manner. Finally, Darin laughed and ran away, leaving Robby to do the entire job himself.

When his father arrived home, he noticed the floor was not as neatly swept as Robby usually swept it. Thin sawdust lines ran along the floor. He went upstairs and asked Darin and Robby to explain why the cellar was not cleaned to his standards.

"I worked very hard," Darin said coldly, "but Robby did not. He was lazy." He said it with smug satisfaction.

"Go to the attic," his father said to Robby.

Darin got a new bike, but Robby did not. When Robby saw Darin riding his new bike, he became enraged. He waited in Darin's bedroom for him to come inside. When Darin finally walked into the bedroom, Robby said, "Why did you lie to our father? You got a bike, and I didn't. I did all the work."

Darin ran to Robby, picked him up and threw him over the bed. The back of Robby's head slammed against the radiator. A tremendous pain shot through his head. His eyes rolled backward. He went into convulsions and passed out. He lay unconscious. He heard his mother talking to him but was unable to respond.

"You must stop doing this to your brother, Darin!" she said.

Robby did not move. He lay still.

"Don't tell your father what you did," she said to Darin. "You must keep this a secret."

She helped Robby to Darin's bed, lay him on it, and made Darin leave the room. Robby was aware of his surroundings. His head pounded. Both his ears buzzed with a loud sound. After some time, he drifted into sleep. His last conscious thought was that he might not wake up.

After a week of languishing in bed, Robby sat up. His head hurt. The back of his head was sensitive to touch. He returned to school. The black and blue bruises circling his eyes were so apparent that his teachers noticed. Yet no one stepped up to help him. Robby did his best not to be noticed, but the ringing in his ears was so loud he could not concentrate on his studies.

Robby thought Darin would kill him. He silently plotted his revenge. Finally, one day, he seized the moment.

While Darin was taking a shower in the cast-iron bathtub, Robby snuck into the room, picked up the weight scale, and hit the top of Darin's head with it. Then he put the scale back on the floor and left the room.

When Darin woke up, he could not recall how he had been injured. He was taken to the doctor for treatment but arrived home safely. No one asked questions. Darin suspected he slipped in the bathtub and hit his head on the edge of the tub.

Robby and Darin continued to fight. Outside, in the backyard, Darin snuck up behind Robby, clamped his hands around Robby's neck and squeezed with all his strength. Robby seized rigid. He struggled to breathe. He gasped, but no air came in. His vision blurred. Robby grabbed Darin's hands and tried to free himself from Darin's tight grip. But he was smaller than Darin and not as strong. Robby wiggled and thrashed. He reached his arms up behind his brother and pounded his fist against Darin's ears. Darin did not let go. Robby slapped his ears harder. He kicked Darin's legs. Finally, Darin released him.

Robby heaved forward, and sucked in every bit of air he could. Every second counted. He took off running, wanting to get as far away from Darin and his father as he could get, charging between houses and through the fields toward the train tracks, jumping over fallen tree branches, and leaping over gullies. He turned along the tracks and raced as fast as his legs would allow, hearing the chug of an approaching train, its whistle closing in on him. Robby believed the devil himself was going to engulf him, just run him over, trample him so no one ever knew he even existed. The train roared by him, sending a tremendous rush of wind toward him, almost lifting him off his feet. He embraced its wickedness, the loose leaves flying around him, the dirt swooping up from the ground, the little stones kicking at his ankles. The train ran and ran endlessly with him, its sound drowning out the rest of the world. Robby felt as if its energy carried him along, urging him to keep running. He raced on and on, long after the train passed him, long after his legs weakened and his hands opened their clenched fists, his breath finally giving out. When he stopped, he was at the edge of town. He stood still. He looked around him. Someday, he thought, he would get out of this broken-down place that stank of dead clams and metal. He looked at the smokestacks in the distance. The dirty, toxic fumes dulled the blue sky. But up higher, the sun shone like a beacon, sending its rays toward him as if reaching for him. The river, just beyond the train tracks, flowed toward something better, rippling, glistening, rocking, leisurely traveling in a carefree manner, slapping at the land's edges, letting the movement of life just be. He wanted that.

But first, he had to prepare himself for the fight for his life.

He turned around and made the long trek home. Once there, he hurried into the attic and locked himself in.

The next day, Darin snuck up to Robby with a rake and swung its end into his back. The force hit Robby so hard that he passed out on the ground. When he awoke, he lay still. He wanted to cry out for someone to come help him, but no one came. When he was finally able to, he stood and stumbled up to the attic, where he lay with bruised ribs for an entire day.

Two days later, he stepped out the attic door and down the long steps. He went through the kitchen and out the door to the open sunshine. He walked around the backyard. Suddenly, Darin struck Robby's head with the back of a hammer. Robby ran back into the attic. A huge lump swelled on his head. A few days later, he ventured out, wanting revenge. He saw Darin in the front yard. He got the rake from the garage. He snuck up to Darin and swung it into his back, punching holes into his skin. Then he ran back into the house.

His father sat in his living room chair, reading his magazine. He looked at Robby. "Go to the attic!"

Robby scrambled to the attic, the place that was both his sanctuary and his prison. His father was not only his enemy, but his brother was too. If they were really going to kill him, he was not going to make it easy for them.

CHAPTER 7

During the week, when Robby arrived home from school, he took his place alone at the kitchen table, eating the few bites of the food his mother fed him as she worked. The light meals were not enough to fully sustain him. Nancy tried to help. When Robby was locked in the attic, she brought food to the attic from time to time and left it on the floor by the door. They had agreed to a special knock that would let Robby know it was safe to open the door and take the food.

At the end of each day, while sitting in the kitchen with his mother, Robby watched the clock with abnormal intensity, counting the ticking minutes until his father's truck rumbled down the street and pulled into the driveway. Then Robby scrambled up the staircase and through the attic door to be locked away. He dreaded the sound of his father's footsteps in the house, the sound of his booming voice demanding his evening cocktail. From the attic, Robby heard the crinkle of his Father's newspaper as he turned the page while he waited for his dinner to be served. All four of his siblings were quiet. His mother was quiet too.

From below the wobbly, wood-plank floor, Robby heard his mom and dad and four siblings eating dinner together at the kitchen table. Mostly he could hear the utensils clanging around and Nancy giving her stern father a rundown of her day. His mother rarely spoke, but his Father's booming authoritarian voice sent an undeniable shiver of fear up Robby's back. Robby had long ago lost the desire to be at the dinner table with his family. Watching his family eat while he was denied food was too much for him to bear.

The small attic was dark. Without a heater, Robby was cold. When he stood up, his concaved abdomen bent like a thin branch forced down in a brutal wind. He lifted a floorboard and took out a candle and some matches he had hidden there. He set the candle on his small wooden chair and lit it. On the floor in the corner, he picked up a paper bag and folded it into a pirate hat. He placed the hat on his head, picked up a handmade sword he had made from scraps of wood in his father's wood shop and faced the wall. The candle cast a light on the wall. Robby saw a shadow of himself, but this shadow was not him. It was Robby's one true friend. They were pirates together, holding swords, about to spar for the sheer joy of it. This friend never hurt Robby when he swung his sword, and Robby never hurt him, either. Robby gallantly lifted his sword and began his duel with his friend, slashing his sword back and forth, stepping forward and backward in an assertive manner. As he fought, his mood elevated, and his inner resolve grew. His best friend fought to fortify Robby's strength. For half an hour, Robby swiftly waved his sword, working to develop quicker reactions and build his defenses. The more he fought, the more confident he became.

Finally, he grew tired. He put his pirate hat and sword down and took out his button box from behind his mattress. Finding an old pair of scissors, he cut out a fierce wolf and a Little Red Riding Hood paper doll from some pieces of cardboard he had found in his father's cellar and kept. Next, he cut out a woodsman character holding an axe and then cut out Little Red Riding Hood's Grandmother. Each one wore paper clothing and hats. He used wire to tie the figures to wooden sticks. He held them up to the lit candle to create an image of his creations against the wall. He began acting out the story of Little Red Riding Hood. He knew the story by heart and had all the characters ready.

When he was done, Robby put the stick characters down and blew out the candle. The evening had settled in. Downstairs he listened to his mother washing the dinner dishes. His brother and sisters, and father were silent. Even Alice was quiet. Robby went to the door handle and wiggled it to make sure it was locked. He removed the floorboards next to the door and eased down into a long, enclosed space at the back of the staircase that led down to the cellar floor. Using his arms, he descended very slowly and quietly, like a monkey, knowing his family was just on the other side of the wooden stairs. Once he reached the cellar, he quietly dropped down onto the floor. He hurried past his father's lathe machine and table saws and rows of various kinds of wood piled against the wall. At the end of the shop, he climbed the small set of stairs and pushed open the angled door to the outside. He was as quiet as a mouse as he stepped outside and slowly closed the cellar door. He faced the dark night.

The temperature was cool but not cold enough to make him regret going outside. The Riverside spring season was warming the temperature to bearable, and he did not mind the chilly breeze. He walked along the back of the other houses and rummaged through the neighbor's garbage cans but did not find much worth keeping. He went into a neighbor's vegetable garden and searched around it. Although harvested and waiting for the spring season to replant, Robby's digging always paid off. He found some frozen, scattered snow peas lying on the ground and put them in his pants pocket. He dug in the ground and found some earthworms, which he put in another pocket. He headed back.

Before he went back through the cellar door, he spied his family through the windows. His mother had finished the dinner dishes and was sitting at the kitchen table, looking through her Betty Crocker cookbook. Even though she had added some extra pounds and wore her light brown hair short to her chin, she was still a beautiful woman with her raised cheekbones, pink lips, and blue eyes. Robby watched her for a while and then went to the living room window, where he saw his father sitting in a chair reading a magazine. His siblings were in their bedrooms.

Robby walked to the cellar door and opened it. He made his way across the room and climbed the back of the staircase to the attic. Once inside the attic, he rummaged through his button box for a jar with a punctured lid and put the worms in it. He then plugged the drain into his sink and filled it with water. He opened one side of the peapods and took the peas out of them. With the peapod shells, he fashioned several little, green canoe-like boats and floated them in the water. He shot the little peas at the boats as if he were bombing wartime ships. This entertained him for a long time.

Finally, compounded by poor eyesight and no corrective glasses, he could no longer see in the dark, so he emptied the sink and set aside the little peapod boats. He used the toilet and lay down on his mattress. He wondered what had led to this moment for him to be left to be so alone, so motherless and fatherless, how he was left to cope with hunger and wounds that seemed to come from the inside out. He felt as if he had slowly been hacked at until he was just a shell of himself, hidden away for no one to ever know. Although he had yet to see the face of death, he often wondered if he would see it soon. But he did not want to die, not here, not like this. Finally, he fell asleep, but he slept fitfully, tossing and turning, his injuries making him uncomfortable.

The early dawn came through the lone window in the attic and awakened Robby. He used the toilet and then picked up the jar of worms and looked at them. They wiggled frantically around. He carried the jar to the windowsill and carefully opened the window. The cool air rushed in. He opened the jar and pulled out the worms. Then he lined the windowsill with the worms and stepped back into the corner, and waited. After a couple of minutes, two sparrows arrived and began eating the worms. Robby fed them every morning. The sparrows had begun to trust him enough to stick around and let Robby near him. Although he never petted him, he believed he had a special friendship with them.

An hour later, he watched his father's car pull out of the driveway and drive down the road for work. A while later, his mother knocked on the attic door. He opened it, and she gave him some oatmeal.

"Come to the kitchen today and eat with all of us," she urged him.

"No." Robby quickly shut the door and locked it. He ate in silence.

After a while, his sister, Nancy, came up into the attic to take Robby to school. She helped him look more presentable by putting a light jacket over his dirty shirt and buttoning it. Today was the end of the third quarter grading period, which meant Robby would be bringing home his report card. This filled him with dread, knowing his grades would not meet his father's expectations. His brother and sisters would be praised for their scholarly achievements, while he would be forced into more weeks of confinement in the attic and denied his dinner.

Robby took a deep breath and walked with his sisters to school. Although he could not concentrate well enough to learn and wiggled too much in his chair, he always tried his best to please his teacher. At least he could do that.

CHAPTER 8

When the summer break began, the family drove to Nova Scotia to visit Uncle Irving and Aunt May on their farm. Once there, Pearl became happy. She spent her days helping Aunt May in the kitchen. They cooked the entire day making three meals for the family. To make himself useful, Robby's father walked around the farmhouse, fixing windows and repairing furniture.

Robby and Darin played outside behind the store. Uncle Irving let them use his bows and arrows to shoot at a hay pile. The boys shot the arrows over and over into the hay. Darin, just a short distance from Robby, shot his arrows at Robby several times with just enough force to pierce his skin. Robby ignored him. The past summer, Uncle Irving had taught Robby how to use the bow and arrow. He taught him how to pivot and squat while at the same time pulling the bow back to get ready to shoot. Robby knew he could shoot his brother, but he did not want to. But Darin continued to shoot arrows at him. Robby grew tired of it. He spun around toward his brother, lowered himself to the ground, pulled the arrow back on the bow, and aimed it at Darin. His brother was so close that if he shot it, he could kill Darin. But Nancy, who was photographing the brothers, told Robby not to do it. Robby relaxed the bow, stood up, pivoted, and shot the arrow at the hay. After that, Darin left him alone.

After a week, Robby's mother and father packed up the kids and left, leaving Robby at the farm for the summer. Once alone with his aunt and uncle, Robby helped Aunt May in the kitchen. He also worked in the store, selling supplies to the other farmers. He helped Uncle Irving with the outside farm work. After the work was completed, he wandered the great vast land, sliding through the tall grasses, greeting nature's hidden wonders - grasshoppers, ladybugs, beetles, grass snakes, mice, muskrats. He climbed trees and spent hours pretending to soar with the great hawks and eagles. Perched high in the branches, he gazed at the brilliant, dancing ocean that stretched past the land and watched the mighty ships float by. He believed nature spoke to him in the rhythm of wrestling leaves, the birds calling above him, and the squirrels chirping at the base of the trees. He believed the squirrels were telling him to leave their tree alone, but Robby could not. He wanted to be part of this world. He needed to be, so he held onto his spot in the crook of two branches, his legs dangling and swaying. There he was capable and strong. There he lived among the free air that allowed him to gasp its energy and brush gently against his tender skin. There, he was a friend to the slightest insect that inched up the tree and gave him no trouble. Robby's bright blue eyes, blurred as they were with poor eyesight, took in all he could collect and store in his memory. There he learned his greatest lessons in life, that every seedling, every blade of grass, every leaf that fluttered from the tree, was meant to be there, and he too was meant to be a part of the great land. He belonged among the greatest of every bird that soared in the sky, every clap of thunder, every lightning strike brought down on the land. He was Robby of the great Nova Scotia land - navigator, explorer, wanderer, and proud to be a part of something he finally understood. He belonged, if only on this great land, sitting in a tree. Time would be his one true gift. He was certain of this. Glimpses of love were everywhere in Nova

Scotia, in his aunt May's gentle touch, and his uncle's patient education on how to work the land. Like a kaleidoscope of moving images, something was becoming clear and recognizable. He was shifting. The hurt was seeping out, and a new person was emerging.

One day, his uncle took him to the river. "I'm going to show you how to catch a fish." He walked along the stream, looking down at the running water. The bottom of the stream was filled with marble-sized pebbles that squished around in the current. But in other places, the water ran over large, protruding rocks. In between the rocks, there was sand instead of pebbles. "The big rocks push the current around them, leaving the space between them free for the water to remain still. This creates sand and gives the fish a spot to rest from the rushing current. Now watch me." Uncle Irving lay down beside the stream on his belly, turned his face away from the stream, and placed his hand, palm down, in the stream where the still waters sat between the rocks. Then he lifted his fingers slightly and dangled them just above the sand. "Shhh," he said to Robby.

Robby crouched down next to his uncle and watched his uncle's hand. He waited for a brief time until a large trout stopped just under his uncle's hand. He quickly closed his fist. "Gotcha!" Uncle Irving lifted his hand out of the water and revealed the squirming fish. He sat up and handed it to Robby. "This would make a mighty, tasty meal. Now be a good lad and throw the fish back into the river."

Robby squatted by the river and carefully let the trout go into the river.

"Now you try it." Uncle Irving stood. "Use the same spot. It may take a while. You will know you've caught a fish when its fins tickle your fingers. Good things come to those who wait. The rocks give a hungry man who has no other means of getting food a chance to seize a quick meal."

Following his uncle's lead, Robby lay down and placed his hand in the water just as his Uncle had taught him.

"Leave your fingers above the bottom," Uncle Irving said.

The cool water sent a shiver from Robby's hand up his arm. He stayed as still as he could, letting the sun warm the rest of his body. His patience finally paid off. A small trout swam inside his open hand. Robby did not hesitate. Quickly, he closed his fist around the slimy fish. Immediately, the fish began thrashing. He pulled it from the water and sat up.

"Now there's a mighty fine trout," Uncle said.

Robby held it up and looked at it.

"Go ahead and put it back," Uncle Irving said.

Gently, Robby placed his hand in the water and opened his fist. The fish quickly swam off.

"Now you can fish with just your hand, son." Uncle Irving affectionately tapped Robby's shoulder. "Fish are tasty when you have nothing else to eat."

Before dawn the next morning, Robby got up early and left the house, carrying one of Aunt May's small baskets. He walked toward the stream to fish the way his uncle had taught him, hoping to surprise his aunt and uncle with some fish to fry for breakfast. He went to the exact spot Uncle Irving had taught him to fish the day before. The wind whipped along the top of the stream, creating ripples. The water swirled around the rocks, but between them, the water was still, just like his uncle had shown him. He lay on his stomach on the damp ground and placed his hand into the stream between the two rocks. The water was cold, but he held his fingers just over the sand. He caught one quickly, pulling it out of the water and placing it in the basket. He caught another, then another, then another. Within a half hour, he had caught six small trout. Satisfied, he stood, picked up his basket, and walked back to the house, cradling his basket and his prize. He burst into the house and held out his basket.

"There you are, Bobby-boy!" his uncle said. "We were wondering where you went."

"I went fishing for breakfast." Robby handed Aunt May the basket.

Aunt May looked inside it. She burst into a wide smile. "My! What a catch you have." She showed Uncle Irving the fish.

"You did it, Bobby-boy! Good for you!"

Robby beamed with happiness. He had contributed to the meal. He was proud of himself.

"May," Uncle Irving said, "fry up the fish for Bobby-boy! His reward! Give them all to him! He deserves them after his hard work. Sit down, Bobby-boy!"

Robby sat at the table and, along with his uncle, watched Aunt May slice up the fish. They were smaller than sardines, but she managed to cut out small portions of meat and fry them for Robby. When the fish was cooked, she put the pieces on the plate and brought them to him. Six small, fried slices lay on the plate.

"You earned that delicious meal, Bobby-boy," Uncle Irving said. "After breakfast, we will go into the woods. I have some more tricks to teach you."

Robby quickly ate the fish pieces. They were tasty. "Let's go," he said to his uncle.

Uncle Irving and Robby walked through his 100-acre oceanfront land. They swished through the tall grass, past the pink, blue, and yellow wildflowers that dotted the damp ground. Uncle Irving stopped at the base of some maple trees and looked up. "Look up at the trees, Bobby-boy. See how the different tree branches reach one another. They overlap. It is even hard to tell which branches belong to which trees."

Robby looked up. Uncle Irving was right. The branches wound together like arms linked together. "I see that."

"We have a lot of trees on our land, Bobby-boy. "

Robby looked at the hundreds of trees. They stretched forever on the land and beyond.

"See how some of the trees have lines that run up the bark? Others are smooth."

"Yes, I can tell the difference," Robby said.

"See the small branches that grow out of them?" Uncle Irving said. "Those branches are strong enough for you to pull yourself up them with your hands and stand on." Uncle Irving pointed to some of the smaller limbs sticking out of the massive trees. You can grab a limb and pull your entire body up the tree."

"I know, Uncle. I climb trees at home all the time," Robby said.

They walked until they stood at the bottom of a cluster of maple trees. One lone weeping willow tree grew alongside the maple trees. "Here we are," Uncle Irving said. "The Willow trees are the best trees to climb. And the maples will give us the branches we need. You go first."

Robby climbed up the willow tree, stepping on the protruding branches. He lifted his legs and climbed as if he were climbing a ladder. He was fit and strong and able to reach the highest spot in the trees. Uncle Irving followed him.

Uncle climbed up onto a branch next to him. "See how these branches from the maple trees intertwine? That is the perfect spot for our platform house. Watch me." He moved from the willow tree branch onto a maple tree branch and then moved among the branches from tree to tree. "Come on, Bobby-boy."

Robby followed him, gripping the wide branches, inching along on his knees, winding through the tangle of tree branches, carefully moving from one branch to another.

Uncle Irving pointed to the paths the animals made through the forest land. "See where the grass is lying down?"

"Yes," Robby said, peering down at the animal path.

"We could stay up here all day and watch the bears and deer walk along that path. The animals never look up, so they will never know we are here."

Robby stared at the pathway and watched. Soon a doe and her fawn appeared. They walked right under the tree where Robby and his uncle sat and began munching on some nearby brush. Robby and his uncle watched it.

When the deer left, Uncle Irving said, "That is not the reason I brought you here. Let's get down from the trees."

They moved through the branches until they reached the willow tree. "Just grab a branch and let it gently drop you to the ground. Watch." Uncle Irving grabbed a willow branch and gently lowered himself to the ground. He looked up at Robby. "Your turn."

Robby followed his lead. He grabbed a willow tree branch and gripped it. He stepped off the maple tree branch and let his body dangle while the branch lowered him to the ground.

"There you go," Uncle Irving said. "Now, I will show you how to build a platform treehouse out of branches. Help me collect some of the fallen tree branches."

Together they picked up fallen, thick, long branches and laid them next to each other on the ground. One by one, they carried them up a willow tree and found a perfect spot among a cluster of thick maple branches to lay them next to each other, forming a large platform that would hold them. They climbed down the tree and collected old thin, willow tree branches off the trees and carried them up to their platform. They used the branches like rope to weave them in and out of the thick branches to secure the platform together. The platform was sturdy enough to withstand both their weights. They scrambled back down the tree and collected pine boughs with soft needles. They carried them up to the platform and laid them over it, creating a soft, comfortable place to lie and sit on. They climbed down the tree and collected large tree leaves scattered on the ground. They carried the bunches up the tree and laid them across the platform to further soften the floor. Once they were finished, they climbed down the tree and looked up at their platform. Hidden amongst the branches, it was indistinguishable from the trees. They had created their own hidden treehouse.

"I have one more thing to show you," Uncle Irving said.

Robby followed him as they made their way through the forest back to the farmhouse. Uncle Irving stopped in a hemlock grove. The huge trees rose high. Large, thick pine branches stooped downward like massive bird wings toward the ground. At the base of the trees, the first branches reached the ground.

Uncle Irving bent down by a trunk of a hemlock tree and crawled underneath the drooping branches. "Come inside," he called to Robby.

Robby followed him in and sat next to his uncle. "You can build a fort underneath this massive branch, right by the trunk. Come on. I will show you." He climbed out.

Robby followed. Uncle Irving showed Robby how to push the pine needles that were scattered around into the hidden space under the pine branch at the base of the trunk. Then they went inside and dug enough ground away to make a nice hidden spot. The pine needles provided a nice soft cushion to sit on.

"Best of all," Uncle Irving said, "is that when it rains, this shelter will keep you dry. It will also keep you warm in the winter."

Robby looked around the secret spot. He felt safe there.

They returned to the farmhouse to enjoy a big meal Aunt May had cooked for them. Afterward, tired from their day's work, they sat by the fire for the evening to rest. Uncle Irving picked up a dead hemlock stick he had collected that day and began rolling it over and over in his fingers. He kept a steady pace, patiently rolling it until the entire bark slid off the stick. He put the bark down and then carved little grooves into the stick. He put the stick down and picked up the perfectly intact bark. He carved matching grooves into the bark and then slid the stick back inside the bark like he was sliding a pencil into a straw.

"I made a flute." He held it up for Robby to see. He put the end of the flute to lips, placed his fingers over the grooves and blew. The flute produced a sound. He lifted his fingers one at a time. Each time a new tone came out. He played a little melody. When he was done, he gave the flute to Robby. "For you," he said.

Robby placed the flute on the bedstand beside his bed and went to sleep. In the morning, Robby and Uncle Irving awakened before sunrise, ate a hearty breakfast, and hiked to their platform. They climbed up the tree and sat on it. They waited. Before long, a strong, full-grown buck with long antlers walked right beneath them.

Uncle Irving whispered to Robby, "Remember. The stag never looks up. Even though the buck is very alert, he will never look up in the trees."

They were twenty feet up in the tree, and the deer had no idea they were there.

"The pine scent takes the human scent away," Uncle Irving whispered. "The animals will never know we are there."

They lay on the platform, watching deer pass below them. Finally, a bear came foraging through the forest and stopped directly under Robby and Uncle Irving. It never looked up at them. The bear never even knew they were there.

Another day, Uncle Irving hitched Barney on the wagon and took Robby for a wagon ride to the farm fields. The vast fields stretched over rolling hills and were sectioned off for each type of plant that was grown on the farm. They rode to the hay bales already rolled up into huge bundles. Some would feed Barney during the winter months, and some would be sold to the neighbors. Uncle Irving and Robby loaded the bales onto the wagon. Barney pulled the wagon to the barn, and they stored the bales for the winter in the barn. They walked back to a field of harvested corn stalks. The corn was already stored in the root cellar.

"I have to test the soil to see what to plant during the next planting season." Uncle Irving leaned down and tasted the soil to see if it was suitable for next year's crop. "The soil acidity will help me determine which crops to plant where on the field."

Uncle Irving tasted the soil in different sections and made decisions about where to plant next year's crops. "You know, Bobby-boy. It is good to get educated in school, but real happiness comes from living your life honorably and working hard. Remember, quitting difficult jobs is easy, but if you quit, then it is over. You cannot win if you quit. Why not keep working at it to see where it leads, no matter the obstacles?" He patted Robby on his back and then led him back to the farmhouse.

Uncle Irving took Robby bareback riding on Barney, into the woods. As they galloped, Robby hung onto the horse's mane, secure between the horse's neck and Uncle Irving's strong body. They galloped until they were deep into the woods, surrounded by trees with immense tree trunks. They ducked through the tangles of the branches reaching down on them, rushing through the enchanted forest where the sun shone above. The wind whistled. The cool wind rushed the scent of the pine trees up Robby's nostrils. The biting wind exhilarated him, made him limber and free. At the creek, they dismounted. Robby grabbed a thin branch that was lying on the ground and held its tip into the running stream.

Uncle Irving said. "You are an explorer now. When you are grown, you will appreciate what I have told you. You will remember that I was the only person who told you the truth about your life. You are special. You shall see." Uncle Irving smiled widely, looking mighty pleased to have Robby on the farm with him. "You shall see," he repeated.

Uncle Irving spent the rest of the day with Robby, showing him how to track deer and bears, and how to sit quietly by the streams to wait for the bears. "If you stay very quiet, the bears will ignore you while they fish."

They sat on rocks by the stream, sitting still and silent, waiting for the bears to venture into the stream. After a while, a mother bear came out of the forest and approached the other side. A while later, her two cubs strolled out from the trees and tumbled around the grass while their mother fished for their food. Uncle Irving and Robby watched in awe at the magnificent sight. When the bears retreated into the forest, Uncle Irving led Robby back to Barney. Uncle Irving lifted Robby onto Barney's back and then mounted behind him. On the way back to the farm, Barney threw a shoe. Robby and Uncle Irving dismounted and walked Barney home.

Once home, they brought Barney to the blacksmith shop in the barn. Robby watched Uncle Irving heat a metal shoe and then set it aside to cool.

"Did you learn all this stuff in school?" Robby asked him.

Uncle Irving paused for a minute. "There are two types of school," he finally said. "One school is where you're going that teaches you to cipher and how to read and write, so you can read the newspaper and when you go down to the mercantile, you know how much change you're going to get back." He hesitated.

"What's the second school, Uncle?"

"The second school is where you learn about life. Without that, the rest of it does not matter. Ciphering is not enough. You must know how to survive. You must understand nature because it is equally as important to learn what nature is going to bring to you as it is to know how to cipher and read a newspaper. You must know where you are going to get your food. Even though I am weak at ciphering, I know how to survive. I study nature. If you see a bear feeding its young, it's the order of nature. Learn from it. Look at the trees and determine how severe the winter is going to be. You can tell by watching the changing leaves. All the signs you need to know are there for you to observe. You must learn how to keep yourself alive. No one will hand you anything. Later in life, you will remember me and thank me for what I have told you. I am the only person who told you the truth about who you are. You are an explorer, an adventurer. You are special, unlike all the others. A warrior lives inside of you. Now remember what I say to you."

Robby soaked in his uncle's words as if he were a sponge deprived of water. He stood a little taller and walked with more confidence. Looking at the land, he saw how he was connected to it. He saw that he could be a part of it.

Although still young, Robby explored the land on his own. He wasn't afraid. The wind beckoned him. The sun warmed him. The scent of the grasses and trees filled his senses. He believed the land and animals were all his own, that he was as much a part of the land as the creatures that roamed it. As he wandered, he knew instinctively that his survival was his own responsibility. He carefully marked his walking trail with piles of rocks so he could retrace his steps back to the farmhouse. After a while, he came across a deep gurgling stream, spilling over protruding, large rocks. Long grass stems grew up from the side of the stream. He went to its edge and watched the water lapping and winding down the stream, creating a rhythmic sound of natural music that soothed his ears. He noticed a trout swimming in the water. Dragonflies hovered above the water.

Then two bear cubs appeared across the stream. They wandered along its edges, unaware of Robby's presence. Robby stooped down and froze. His uncle had warned him that if he ever saw bear cubs stand perfectly still because the mama bear would hurt him to protect her cubs. The mama bear appeared from the brush and lumbered toward her cubs. Robby took quiet, shallow breaths. The mama bear went to the stream and began pulling fish from it with her big paw. She fed them one by one to her cubs. Robby was afraid at first, but after a while, he began to feel safe. The mama bear did not charge him. She scooped up a large fish and put it in her own mouth, and chewed it, watching Robby. Then she split the mushed fish out on a rock, waddled out of the stream, and took her cubs back into the brush. When they were gone, Robby stood. He believed the bear did not attack him because he was small like her own cubs. He also believed the bear left him the chewed-up fish as a present. He believed the bear had signaled to him that she was his friend. Robby was overjoyed. He turned back to the farmhouse. His day was complete. He had his rock signs to guide him back to his uncle and aunt, who loved him.

CHAPTER 9

Robby returned home from Nova Scotia, a different person. His body was stronger. He had gained weight. He walked taller. He was no longer a rag doll monkey that could be punched around the room. He had substance. He carried his uncle's words inside of him. He was a person who belonged. He was lovingly greeted by his mom but faced a standoffish reception from his brother. On the second day, he was allowed outside to be near his father. He quietly played in the dirt, avoiding his father but at the same time wishing his father would acknowledge him. More than anything in the world, he wanted a father who loved him. He hoped his father had missed him and was glad he had returned home.

His dad finally said, "Robby, you can invite your friends over. We can have a get-together to celebrate your return home."

The prospect of his neighborhood friends coming over delighted Robby, and he quickly invited them to his house. Before they arrived, he spent time thinking up games they could play. He planned to play hide-and-seek with them and feed them peanut butter and jelly sandwiches and Kool-Aid to drink. When they arrived at his house, Robby gathered his friends into his backyard and began his day's events.

But before he got started, his father came out the door and went straight to his friends. From the angry look on his father's face, Robby knew something bad was going to happen.

"You boys," his father said. "I want you all to go home and never come back." He waved his arms toward the street.

"You hear me! Get! Get! Don't come back!" He grabbed Willie and Donnie by their hair and banged their foreheads together. They cried out in pain. Then he turned to Robby and backhanded the back of his neck. Robby flew forward, his face slamming into the ground. His friends fled the yard, running at top speed to get away.

After they were gone, his father picked Robby up by his ear, yanked him into the house, and tossed him down the stairs to his cellar workshop. "This is what you're doing today. Clean this place until it's spotless."

Robby waited until his father left before he let tears sting his eyes. It was a while longer before he could pull himself up to a standing position. He surveyed the room. His Father had intentionally left a mess. Sawdust was everywhere. It would take him hours to make the room look perfect again. When he was finally able to begin the work, he gingerly moved. His head hurt. He discovered one tooth was now loose. Slowly, he worked, bending down to scoop the sawdust onto the dustpan. When he was done sweeping, he mopped the floor. He wiped off all his father's wood-cutting machines. He stacked and organized all the strips of wood. When he was finally finished cleaning the mess, he crawled into the end corner of one of his Father's saws and curled into a ball. He fell asleep.

A noise jarred him awake. He looked up and saw his father walking around the room. His benign expression did nothing to ease Robby's terror. To him, his father was a wolf. Fear gripped him. He tried to make himself smaller, curling up into himself, hiding his face in his hands. A while later, his father turned on one of his saws and began cutting a piece of wood. The loud, grinding sound, along with his father's back facing Robby, gave Robby the perfect opportunity to watch him work. After a while, he eased out from his hiding place and tiptoed to the doorway. There, he climbed to the space behind the back of the stairs and disappeared into the secluded space of the house. He climbed up the stairs until he reached the safety of the attic. There, he collapsed on his bed and fell into a deep sleep.

When he awoke, he went to his sink and turned on the water. He took his first sip of water in hours, then carefully washed the blood from his face. His front tooth was loose. He lay back down, feeling defeated and alone. A while later, he heard a knock on the door and knew it was Nancy's special knock. She must be sneaking food to him. He got up, unlatched his lock, and opened the door. She was no longer there, but on the floor was some bread and oatmeal. He picked it up, brought it into the attic, placed it on the floor, and relatched the lock so no one could enter. He picked up the food and tried to eat it. His mouth didn't chew right. It hurt to chew. He ate what he could and then sank into his bed for the day. Despair filled him. But then he imagined riding bare-back on a horse with his uncle in Nova Scotia. In the vivid recreation, he was there, racing with the cool wind on his cheeks, the feel of his uncle's safe embrace, and he was invincible again, strong, powerful, and able to survive anything. The land stretched out before him. It was his land, his open space that no one, not even his father, could take away from him. The birds, flying high in the blue sky, beckoned to him. Rabbits fled from the horse's path. The pines scent soothed him. All Robby had to do was close his eyes, and he was there, free and happy. He was blessedly safe from his Father.

For the next few days, Robby slept on and off. He stayed in the attic during the daytime while his Father worked at the chemical company. From the thin floorboards, he heard his sisters talking in their bedroom, giggling, playing, and his mother singing Mario Lanza songs and baking in the kitchen. He could go down there if he wanted to visit with his mother, but defeat had settled in him like the plague that threatened to destroy his ability to ever bounce back. The sparrows came to his window in the morning, but he did not feed them. He had no worms.

When he finally ventured downstairs to visit the family, he sat at the kitchen table, where his mother offered him a thin veil of safety. She brought him the button box and put it on the table for him. He thumbed through it, looking for something to invent. Even with his eyes focused on searching through the box, he knew his father had come into the room. He heard his footsteps, and smelled the cocktail he had just consumed. Robby ignored him.

His father walked through the kitchen and then went back to the living room. He yelled to his children, "Terry, Nancy, and Darin! Come coco!"

Robby kept his eyes on the box. He listened to his siblings quickly run into the living room. From where Robby sat at the table, he could see his siblings standing still in the center of the front room.

"Get in a straight line," his father told his three children.

They immediately moved next to each other. Robby kept his eyes on his button box.

"Repeat after me," his father said to his siblings. "See no evil. Hear no evil. Speak no evil."

In unison, his siblings repeated the words.

"Now do it again," his father said. "Terry, you are first. Cover your eyes. Nancy, you cover your ears. Darin, you cover your mouth. Robby, get into the room!"

Robby jumped up and quickly went into the room. His heart pounded. His mouth became completely dry. He licked his lips.

"Stand next to Darin!" his father said.

Robby did as he was told. He stood by his brother, his arms at his side. His hands balled into fists.

"Repeat it the way I said, all together, with your hand gestures," his father said.

The siblings repeated it. "See no evil. Hear no evil. Speak no evil."

Robby did not know what he was supposed to do, so he stood stiff and still.

"Now get out, Robby," his father yelled.

Robby raced into the kitchen, ran up the stairs into the attic, and slammed the door shut. He turned the lock. Several minutes passed before his heart stopped racing.

From then on, his father often made his children repeat the bizarre repetitive saying with hand gestures. The more his father did it, the more Robby realized that his family had a secret. His siblings were being told to keep Robby's abuse a family secret. Robby hated standing in line with them. By standing there, he was allowing his family to keep the secret. One day, he stepped out of line and went back into the attic.

Robby regularly snuck out of the house. His father thought he was locked in the attic, but his mother knew he was sneaking out of the house. She covered for him whenever his escapes were about to be discovered by distracting her husband with something else that he needed to focus on.

One morning, long before dawn, Robby got up from the mattress and relieved himself in the toilet. It was Saturday, and his father was home. His father would be spending his day working in his woodshop, which was impeccably clean from the cleaning Robby had given it. Although hungry, Robby was pleased to be free for the day and would find some way to get food.

No one would come to the attic to check on him for the entire weekend. He grabbed a fishing pole he had earlier retrieved from a neighbor's garbage can and tucked it in his underclothes. He went to the opening on the floor. He lifted the floorboards and dropped down into the space behind the stairwell. Like a silent snake, he made his way down the back of the stairs, using his hands to descend until he reached the bottom floor. Once in his father's workshop, he stealthily hurried across the floor to the stairs that led upward to the cellar door. Slowly, he opened the door and slipped outside. The cool air invigorated him. He sprinted to the pine trees behind the house. A few nights ago, he had collected pine boughs and made a nest that looked exactly like a squirrel's nest in the tall branches of the trees where he could store his clothes. He put his fishing pole against the tree. Quickly, he climbed the tree to retrieve his clean clothes, his pocketknife, and some rope. From inside the pine needle nest, he took out a pair of pants, a shirt, and a sweatshirt and rolled them under his arm. Then he hid his nest from being discovered by rearranging the pine needles to look like a squirrel's nest and scurried down the tree trunk. He quickly dressed, picked up his fishing pole, and ran behind his house to the train tracks. He followed the train tracks for one and a half miles to Barrington. Only the moon was privy to his pre-dawn escape.

He snuck onto the mill yards in Barrington and sat down at the mill pond. His Uncle Irving had told him that when he became a part of nature, it became part of him. Robby scanned the forested trees looming above him, their leaves rustling in the slight breeze, the early morning light peeking through the branches above. He believed the croaking frogs were talking to him, the birds chirped only for him, and the fish jumped only to be in his presence. He picked up his fishing pole and reached into his pocket, drawing out a worm. He attached it to an old hook he had retrieved from his button box. The casting device was broken, so he dropped the hook into the water and held it onto the end of the pole. He stared at the light rhythmic movement of the waves on the wind-whipped pond and let the swaying tree branches in the early dawn shimmy for him.

Finally, after a long while, he caught a fish. He pulled it up and saw a big bass. Robby laid the fish on the ground and retrieved a pocketknife from his pocket. He cut the fish's head off and then sliced it. He lifted the raw slices and put them in his mouth. He let the cold piece slide down his throat. He ate all the meat on the fish and then put another worm on the hook and dropped a line into the water. By morning, he had eaten four fish. He lay in the tall grass and slept, free of worry and free of hunger.

When he awoke, he stared up at the tree branches intertwining above him, weaving in and out of each other. He could build his own tree platform. He stood and climbed up a weeping willow tree to the spot near a grove of maple trees. The branches from the maple trees weaved together. He stepped across the maples' intertwining branches like a monkey does in the wild. For more than an hour, he practiced weaving through the top tree branches, feeling as if he were on top of the world. He climbed down to the ground and began collecting broken branches. Carrying them, one at a time, up the tree, he lined them next to each other in the crotch of some strong, interconnecting branches. When he had made a sturdy platform, he took some rope from his pants pocket and tied the branches together to create the perfect tiny home for him. He worked swiftly, securing the platform's strength by weaving the rope through each branch to secure them to one another. He climbed down to the ground and collected smaller branches and leaves, and laid them below the tree. He collected pine boughs and put them in the pile too. Then, slowly, he carried his bundle of leaves and boughs up to his platform and laid them across it. He made several trips to complete the task, and by the time he was done, he had a nice soft bed to sit and lie on. He tied a wall of branches along the outer edges to keep him from falling off the platform if he fell asleep. Then he sat down on it. He was so far up the tree that he was invisible to anyone who approached the area. From that high up, he could see across the pond to the river that stretched down Rhode Island. He was the king of Providence. He felt safe. This platform would be his special place. He climbed down the tree and peered up at it. He was pleased to see that the tree branches were already naturally entangled, and his little platform was invisible to the naked eye.

He heard voices nearby. He quickly scrambled up the tree to his platform and hid from view. A group of teenagers walked along the pond, swathing at the brush with their long twigs, chattering away about something Robby could not distinguish. Up above them, hidden from view, Robby felt powerful and in complete control of his life. No one could touch him. The boys walked away. Robby lay for a long time enjoying his new tiny home.

CHAPTER 10

At home, in the evening, his father let his children put on talent shows. The entire family gathered around the living room, and each got up, one by one, stood on a stool, and spoke a poem or told a story. His sisters often sang songs they had learned in school or danced or put on a skit. Everyone listened and clapped when they finished.

Robby wanted to be included. "Is it my turn?" he asked his father.

"You really don't have anything to offer," his father said. "But Darin does."

Darin got up on the stool and told a story. When he was done, the family clapped. Robby clapped, too, as expected of him.

Robby became accustomed to his father's insults. He learned not to respond. Most of all, he refused to cry. He pretended like he didn't care. He pretended like he was not affected. But Robby was beginning to rebel. Maybe it was his new-found home in the trees that gave him his new strength to fight back. Maybe he was just growing tired of it all. But physical pain no longer penetrated him. It was as if his body had become numb to his father's slaps. He enjoyed instigating his father's anger. He liked pushing him over his threshold. When his father blew up at him and slapped him, Robby immediately came back at him, sticking his face in his father's face and staring hard at him, without expression, as if telling his father to do it again. His father backed off and walked away. Robby knew he was starting to win the strange battle he was in with his father. He had found a way to disarm him.

Still, Robby was deeply affected by his father's rage toward him. Although outwardly he stood up to his father, he couldn't quell the emotional pain from surfacing, swelling up inside of him until he felt like he would either explode or suffocate. When it happened, sadness filled every cell of his body. He lay on his attic mattress, sleeping the days away. No one seemed to care.

One day his mother knocked on the attic door. At first, Robby refused to answer, but she persisted. She knocked louder and louder. "Robby!"

Finally, Robby got up from the mattress, went to the door, unlocked it, and opened his door to see his mother smiling at him.

"Guess what!" She enthusiastically clasped her hands together. Wisps of her brown hair fell on her forehead. She wiped her hands on her food-stained apron and smiled. The smell of the bacon she had cooked for her other children that morning permeated the air around her.

Robby didn't respond. He knew better than to buy into any cheerfulness on the part of his family, even his mother, whom he dearly loved.

"Your Father is taking you to Boston to the Red Sox game today. Come with me. We need to get you cleaned up and dressed properly." She beckoned to him with her hand. "Isn't that exciting, Robby?"

A glimmer of hope filled Robby. He had never been to a baseball game before. He hoped his father would treat him to a hot dog. He hoped he would get a Pepsi. He walked downstairs with his mother and took a bath, and dressed in clean clothes that properly fit and did not have holes in them. His mother helped him into a clean jacket. She had an expression that told Robby everything was fine and that this trip was going to be a special treat for him. Robby believed her how he longed to spend time with his father, to be treated like a real son. He hoped he would get an ice cream cone too! And some peanuts!

His Father waited in the living room, reading his newspaper. "Time to go!" he yelled.

Robby cautiously walked into the living room just as his father was folding the newspaper and standing up. Robby's mother smiled and waved to him as they walked out the door and got into his father's car. Darin, of course, was coming too. They sat quietly as the station wagon made its way down the road, out of Rhode Island into Massachusetts, winding toward Boston's Fenway Park. Robby's mind swirled with excitement. This would be his first baseball game. He wanted to ask his father about it, talk to him like he did to Uncle Irving, but he stayed quiet. Robby's suspense and excitement grew. This time his father would be a real dad to him.

They drove to his father's friend's house and picked up Jim, an old Navy buddy, to go along with them. In his city neighborhood, the brick houses were close together. Each house had cement steps that led to the entrances. A group of children played in the street. Robby thought they were close to the ballpark. His excitement grew.

His Father drove a couple of blocks down the road, pulled to the side of the street, and put his gear shift in the park. The motor ran. "Get out," he said to Robby.

Robby was accustomed to his father's harsh approach, so he brushed it aside and did not move.

"Get out," his father repeated.

Robby stiffened.

"Get out now!" his father repeated.

Quickly, not wanting to be backhanded across his face, Robby opened the door and leaped out, landing hard on the cement. He stood on the sidewalk, waiting for his dad to stop his engine and get out too. But then his father quickly pulled away. The exhaust from the car spat on Robby. Darin stared at him out the back window. He smiled and waved goodbye. The car wheels screeched as if joyously reveling in discarding him. Robby was too shocked to respond. Reality slowly washed over him. Had he been left on a foreign city street? No, he could not have been left. Was this a joke? He watched the far end of the road, waiting for his father's car to reappear and take him to the game as promised, but a long time passed. He did not come. Surely, he couldn't have left him. Surely, he would come back. He waited, his hands in his pockets, turning to look at one end of the street and then the other end. His father did not return. He was not coming. The realization crushed him. His heart pounded. The day was cool and windy. He looked down at the street. Could the ballpark be just a block away? If so, he could walk to it and find his father. But he stood for a long time. The neighborhood was rundown. He was scared. What was he going to do?

Finally, he sat down underneath the steps of an apartment entrance and waited for his father. From an opening under the stairs, he watched the street corner, hoping his father would return. But he did not return. He sat for a long time. Hungry, he crossed his arms around his stomach to help alleviate the hollow feeling in the pit of his abdomen. He was frightened and cold. A group of older boys walked toward him on the sidewalk. They walked with confidence, talking and joking with each other. Robby cowered under the stairs, hoping they wouldn't notice him. He kept his eyes on the boys. Something about the way they walked made him feel threatened.

One boy drew close to Robby. His eyes opened wide. Then he narrowed them. He leaned down. "Hey, what are you doing down there?"

Robby quickly climbed out from under the stairs. He stood. Putting his head down, he squeezed past the boys. One grabbed his arm, but he managed to wiggle free. He leapt on the sidewalk and ran.

"Get that kid," one of them yelled.

Behind him, Robby heard their feet slap against the pavement. It sounded like a bunch of spooked, wild horses thundering toward him. Robby raced down the sidewalk, his arms swinging to aid his movements, his legs stretching out as far as he could. Each time his feet met with the pavement on his worn shoe soles, his feet stung. He gasped for air, heaving in and out with tremendous effort. The terror of getting caught spurred him on. To ditch them, he ran between two big buildings. He turned right and ran alongside it. He saw an open door. He charged inside. He scanned the room for a hiding place. The building was abandoned. Wood and debris cluttered the floor. Robby ran into another room, then another. Broken wood, glass, and old shelving were piled on the floor. He lay down and covered himself with the two-by-fours, splintered chunks of wood, broken glass, and an old broken cabinet, covering his body the best he could, Petrified, he lay completely still and quiet.

The boys came into the room. "Where is that runt?" one said.

They walked around the debris. One stepped close to Robby's head. Another shoe stepped near his knee. Luckily, the lighting was so dim that they could not see well. One boy kicked around the wood. Robby held his breath, but his heart pounded furious beats. Finally, the boys left.

Robby lay there for a long time, relieved to be finally safe. Finally, exhaustion washed over him like a faucet releasing his anxiety. Once he relaxed, the weight of fatigue filled every pore of his body. His eyes begged not to close. Still buried under the wooden debris, hidden from the world and all its danger, he succumbed to a relaxed state of consciousness. The familiar scent of the wood soothed him. He could not stop himself. He fell asleep.

He opened his eyes. The air blowing through the broken windows was cooler. Birds chirped in a lone tree out the broken window. Where was he? What happened? He remained still. A heavy two-by-four lay over his legs. A broken cabinet was on top of him. His arm was numb. His thoughts were foggy, but then he remembered. It came thundering back – his father dumping him, the boys chasing him, the building he hid in under all the construction debris. How long had he been sleeping? What day was it? He scanned the site. He listened. No one was in the building. He pushed the wood away, the debris, and the old cabinet and sat up. He stood. His muscles were stiff and sore. Lifting one leg in front of the other, he waded through the debris to the door. Peering outside, he could see the evening settling in. He did not want to be there all night. He had to go back to the spot where he had been dumped earlier in the day.

As he walked back to the road where his father had left him, he hoped the kids were gone. He wished he could make himself invisible. But, of course, that was impossible. He stayed close to the houses, avoiding the sidewalk where he might be seen. People were inside their houses. He scanned his surroundings, trying to catch every movement he saw from the corner of his eye; a tree leaf blowing by him, a squirrel scurrying by. He reached the spot where his father had left him. He waited at the end of the block.

Finally, he saw his father's car coming down the street. He stopped near Robby. He hurried to the car, opened the door, and got into the back seat. Darin sat on the other side, eating a tootsie roll. His father continued driving, a tootsie roll dangling from his lips too. Robby put his head down. He had gone from one dangerous environment right into the clutches of another, even if the scene looked benign, with the tootsie rolls happily being chomped on by his two male family members. He heard their mouths gnawing away on it, but he refused to look at them.

CHAPTER 11

Robby's mother walked into the attic. "You're going to the baseball game again."

Robby sat on his chair, not at all enthused. His shoulders slumped.

"Come on, son," his mother said. "You will have fun! Just you and Darin and your dad."

Robby sat still.

"Get up now and go have fun," she said cheerfully.

Robby stood. He wanted to explain to his mother that his father was dumping him on the city streets on his way to the ballpark. He had yet to attend a game. Instead, he remained silent. He made his way down the stairs and into the kitchen, where the smell of the morning breakfast of pancakes he had been denied still lingered in the air. He went outside and got into his father's car. Darin was already in the car. His father, looking impatient that he had to wait so long for Robby, threw the gear shift into reverse and barreled down the driveway and onto the street. They traveled the usual route, picking up Jim and then dumping Robby on a city street again for the day. Darin watched Robby from the back window as the car sped away. He waved and smiled.

Sitting on the apartment steps, Robby shivered with fright and anxiety. But then Jim's wife, Eileen, pulled up in her car. She opened her passenger door and said, "Get in, Robby. You are coming home with me."

He got in the front seat of her car. As she drove toward her house, Robby sat silent. Tension filled his body.

"Jim told me your dad was dumping you in this neighborhood. I thought I would come to rescue you," Eileen said.

When they arrived at her house, Robby got out of the car and followed her into the house. He was fed soup and a sandwich, cookies, and ice cream.

"Would you like to watch some cartoons on the TV," she asked him.

Robby nodded. He finished his cookie and then followed her to the living room. She turned on the television, and he watched cartoons for the next couple of hours. Although he did not feel completely comfortable, at least he was safe and fed properly.

Later, she drove Robby back to the spot where she had found him so that when his father returned to pick him up, he would not know that she had kept Robby that day. Robby sat on the step of an apartment and waited for his father, his stomach full, his fear minimized, but he was still scared and worried. Worst of all, he was beginning to feel something pitiful stirring around his mind, like a flashing neon sign on the street, warning him of what he was facing, and would always face. He was completely alone in the world.

The next time his father dumped him on the city street and drove off with Darin and Jim to the Red Socks game, Robby did not waste any time. As soon as the car jubilantly careened around the corner and out of sight, Robby walked toward Jim's house. He had remembered the way there and followed the roads to her house, relieved that safety was just within walking distance. When he reached her house, he climbed the steps to the front door and vigorously knocked. He waited, anticipating some bread and soup and Oreo cookies and possibly some ice cream. His stomach rumbled, begging to be filled. She did not answer. He knocked again. She did not answer. After several minutes, he gave the door a slight kick. No response. He sat down on the steps. He reached for a long stick lying on the ground next to a bush and spent some time raking it through the dirt. He scratched spiders with numerous long legs that would launch their escape should they be threatened. He drew birds with massive wings that could soar far away if necessary. He sat all day, imagining the soup and crackers he could be eating if only she came home. But she never came.

The sunset is toward the west. The day was ending. Finally, he stood, threw the stick down, and walked back to the spot where his father had discarded him earlier to wait for him to come to pick him up. He stood by a giant tree, hugging it, feeling weary and hungry. Even his mind was fatigued. His vision was clouded with wet tears. His eyes stared ahead.

He waited and waited. The darkness grew around him. The trees and buildings loomed in the black air. Fireflies twinkled around him. Hunger gripped him. He hoped his father would come to pick him up and take him home. Compared to the unknown city, the hot attic seemed like heaven. But his father never came. Robby decided to walk to the abandoned building nearby. He hurried there. When he reached the empty building, he went inside it. The interior was so dark he stumbled along the debris until he found a secluded spot in a corner. Then he cleared the floor and lay down. He piled wood and any scraps he could find around him and on top of him. He lay, ensconced in the brutal silence and darkness. He forced himself to stay awake.

In the morning, he knew he had to find food. He decided to walk farther north along the sidewalk and see what he could find. He walked a few miles along the city block past more houses and larger buildings until he came to a block with businesses and stores. Posters of women dressed in tight, revealing dresses scaled the buildings' walls. He was shocked to see women like that. He peeked into some nightclubs and restaurants and decided not to go inside them. Trash littered the city sidewalk. Robby walked to the alley behind the restaurants and dug through the trash. He found plates of old spaghetti. He scooped it into his mouth, ravenously chewing and swallowing, filling his stomach as fast as he could, not paying attention to anyone who may be watching him. He ate all the trash food he could find. When he was full, he walked back to the front of the buildings to the sidewalk and walked farther down it. He crossed a busy street and continued walking. Across another street was a YMCA. He walked to it and went inside the entrance, and scooted past the front desk before the employees noticed him. Farther down the hallway, he found a boys' bathroom and went inside. He used the toilet. He walked down a hallway to a door leading to a large pool. Kids swam inside it. He walked to a corner of the pool room, stripped down to his shorts, folded his clothes into a pile, and left them there. He eased into the water. The lifeguards did not stop him. He blended in with the children who splashed around in the water and dove off the diving board. Robby did not know how to swim, so he stayed close to the edge and held onto it. He walked around the shallow end, letting the cool water soothe him. The sun rays danced on the moving water. He waved his arms through the water. He listened to the other children laughing and talking to each other. He copied them. He took a deep breath and immersed his face in the water. Quickly, he pulled his face out of the water and opened his eyes. Water poured from his nose and mouth. He put his face in the water again and left it in the water a little longer. He lifted it out and gasped for air. Then he walked, lifting his legs, casually parting the water to make waves. By the end of the day, he was paddling around the shallow end, his feet off the pool floor. Finally, the pool closed for the day. He got out of the water and got his clothes. He put them on. Then he followed the other children out of the facility to the sidewalk.

Immediately, Robby did not feel safe. He wondered what he should do now. He stood for a while, watching all the children leave for their homes. Robby was too young to be alone. An empty feeling settled inside him. He had nowhere to go. The image of the attic at his parents' house seemed very inviting and safe as he stood exposed on the street.

He put one foot in front of the other and began walking back to the place his father had dumped him. He was hungry, but he decided not to dig in the garbage behind the restaurants again. He only had a few hours of daylight left, and he was in the bad part of Boston. He kept walking, his hunger gnawing at him. Exercise-fatigue saturated his muscles, but he continued, haphazardly weaving around the people. Women solicited men who were hurrying toward the buses. He continued.

He stopped walking. He stood on the sidewalk next to his father's friend, Jim's home. He had no choice but to ask them for help. He shuffled to the front steps, climbed to the front porch, and lifted his hand. He knocked. He waited. No one answered. He knocked louder. If they didn't answer, his only option would be to return to the empty building to sleep for the night. But then the door opened.

Jim stood there. "Hello, Robby."

Robby glanced downward. "Hello."

Eileen came to the door. "Are your parents with you?"

"No." Robby looked up at her.

Eileen's expression changed from bewilderment to a sudden look of understanding. She opened the door. "Come inside. You hungry?"

Robby walked inside and stood by the door.

"Don't be shy. Come in," Eileen said. "Go into the kitchen and sit down at the table."

Shuffling behind her, Robby was at least happy that he was clean and halfway presentable after swimming all day.

Eileen motioned for him to sit down at the table. Robby sat down on the vinyl, red seat and placed his hands on the Formica tabletop and folded them. He was hungry.

"How about some chicken noodle soup with crackers?" Eileen said.

"Good." Robby's stomach rumbled in anticipation. Eileen reached for a can of Campbell's soup and opened it with an electric can opener mounted on the wall.

Jim sat beside Robby and looked at him. Something about him made Robby uncomfortable. It was the way Jim looked at him. He did not smile like Eileen did. Robby knew Jim was his father's best friend. They had been in the Navy together. Everyone fell silent. When the soup was heated, Eileen poured it from the pan into the bowl and brought it to Robby.

"I'll call your mother and tell her you're here," Eileen said.

Robby ate the soup, being careful not to spill it or slurp it down. Eileen went to the telephone mounted on the wall and called his mother.

"Hello, Pearl," Eileen said. "I am fine. How are you?" There was a pause. Robby listened as he ate. "I have Robby here with me." Another pause. "Yes, I will keep him. I am feeding him now." A bit later, "I sure will. Ok. See you. Bye." She hung up the telephone and looked at Robby. "You're spending the night with us."

Robby finished his soup and took the empty bowl to the sink, washed it, and placed it on the drying rack.

"Come to the living room and watch television," Eileen said.

Jim, Eileen, and Robby settled in the living room to watch the small RCA television. Robby sat on a small sofa, and Jim and Eileen sat on matching recliners. They watched the "I Love Lucy" show. Robby became very sleepy. He had gotten little sleep the night before, and the wandering and swimming had worn him out. His eyes closed. He curled in the corner, put his head on the armrest, and immediately fell asleep.

He awakened before it was light. He lifted his head and looked around. He was in Eileen and Jim's house. The living room was dark and silent. He did not want to be there. He sat up and put on his shoes. He stepped out the front door and ran as fast as he could down the block. He kept running. The moon still hung in the sky. Dawn had yet to break. He darted behind the houses, running for blocks and blocks. No one was around. He reached a railroad track. Large bushes lined the side of the tracks. He crawled underneath one and sat down. He pulled his knees to his chest. He sat, shivering more from fright than the cold.

He remembered the time he and some friends had climbed a slow-moving train as it rumbled down the tracks. He wondered if he should try it again. On the drive from Riverside to Boston in his father's car, he had watched the freight trains rumbling down the tracks. He knew which direction the trains took to Riverside. Finally, the sun came up. He stayed hidden under the brush. Trains rushed by him, chugging toward his hometown.

He got out from under the bushes and walked along the railroad tracks toward his home. Some of the freight trains passing by him had some empty flat cars. What if he jumped onto one and rode the train back to Riverside? When a passing freight train slowed down enough for him to feel like he could completely hop onto a flatbed car, he eagerly watched for one to approach. When one did, he ran alongside it, clasped onto a corner rail with his wide hands, and, using the strength of his arms, shoulders, and hips, hoisted his legs up and onto the platform. He had enough strength to throw his entire body onto it. He quickly rolled to the middle of the car to safety. As the train rumbled down the track toward his hometown, he lay on his back, staring at the sky. By the time he reached Riverside, the morning was late. When the train slowed, he jumped off the flat car and landed in the long grass. He rolled down a short hill. He stood and walked home.

When he walked into the back door of the kitchen, he saw his mother at the kitchen counter making potato salad.

She turned to Robby. "Where's Eileen?"

"At her house." Robby shut the door.

She looked at the door. "How did you get home? Who is with you?" She looked perplexed and concerned.

"I went to the freight yard, jumped a train, and came home," Robby said.

"I thought Eileen was bringing you home."

"I didn't wait for her," Robby said.

"Jumping trains are dangerous."

"I was fine," Robby said.

"Did you go to the game?" His mother started to rub her forehead as if easing headache pain.

"No."

"Did you stay with Eileen?" She looked perplexed.

"This time, I did, but I haven't before." Robby said.

His mother looked horrified. "You mean you're not going to the games?"

"I've never been to one," Robby said.

"Not one?" Her eyes widened.

"He leaves me on the street," Robby said.

"Where do you go?"

"In old buildings, under stairwells," Robby said.

She collapsed on the chair and dropped her hands in her lap. She stared at the floor. Her eyes widened, and she drew in a deep breath.

Robby did not wait for her response. He went up the stairs into the attic and locked himself inside. The attic, although sparse and dark, felt familiar and safe. He pulled a candle out of his button box and placed it on a clay plate on the chair. He lit it. He picked up his cardboard sword and sparred with his imaginary shadow friend illuminated on the wall. He slashed the sword back and forth, fighting with all the anger, frustration, and fear that inhabited him. As he struck the air, renewed energy began to fill him. He was an explorer of the great Nova Scotia land, able to survive and fight off any predators, animal or human, including his father, who was the wolf at his door.

A week later, Robby's dad dumped him on a city street in Boston on the way to the baseball game. Darin was with them in the car and was allowed to go to the baseball game.

"If I never see you again, I'll be happy," his father yelled out the window.

As Robby stood on the sidewalk and watched his father drive away, Darin looked out the back car window, pointed his finger at him, and smiled. Robby did not waste any time watching them drive away. He was no longer a victim. He had found a good method of getting back home. He turned and walked to the train tracks. He waited by some trees until he heard a train coming. Then he went to the edge of the tracks and looked at the approaching train. Luck was on his side. The slow-moving freight train rumbled around the bend. The tall grass beside the moving train swayed with the movement of the cars. Robby waited until a flatbed car came into view, and then he trotted along the moving train, feeling the tall grass tickle his legs as he strode. When the flatbed car came closer to him, he picked up the pace. Once he was parallel to it, he mustered all his strength. He grabbed onto the corner bar and swung his legs up and onto the platform. He released his grip on the bar and rolled to the center of the flatcar. He lay, staring at the sky, his body outstretched on the flat surface and watched the trees and the land fly by.

When he reached Riverside, he jumped off the car, landing with a hard jolt on his feet. He fell and rolled away from the moving train. Standing, he brushed himself off and headed to the mill ponds. Once he arrived, he walked around the pond, his feet sinking into the pond's soft edges of dirt and grass. He walked to a small stream that looked like the perfect spot to catch a fish. When he found two rocks large enough to create a current-free space for the fish to rest, he lay down flat on his stomach, dropped his hand into the water and waited for a fish to come to rest underneath it. He waited a long time, but finally, he was rewarded. Quickly, he snatched his fist closed. He had his prize. A small perch. He lifted it out of the water, placed it in the grass, and stood. He picked up the wiggling fish and carried it back to his tree platform. Holding onto the wiggling fish, he climbed to the top of his platform and laid the fish down. He took out a knife and cut the head off, and sliced it in two. He cut it into pieces. He removed the bones. He ate the pieces raw. When he finished, he lay down on the platform and slept. He drifted in and out of his sleep, opening his eyes enough to watch the leaves gently wrestle their soothing sound to him, the sun streaming through the trees, giving him a little warmth. He lay there all day and had no intention of going home to the attic. When the day was done, he picked up a warm blanket he had stolen from his mother's storage area and wrapped it around him. He rested his head on a blanket of pine needles. He could stay there forever.

But before dawn, he walked home. He climbed through the basement cellar door, ran across his father's workshop, and climbed up the back stairwell to the attic. Once inside, he opened the door and found a bowl of oatmeal waiting for him. In addition, Nancy had left him some paper and pencils. He took the bowl, paper, and pencils and brought them into the attic and shut the door and secured the lock. He would have to wait until evening before he could go back outside. In the meantime, he had some paper. He spent his day drawing and cutting out shadow puppets he could use to invent stories with.

CHAPTER 12

Days stretched on. After school was done for the day, he walked home for a short afternoon visit with his mother. Then he retreated to the attic. Winter brought a bitter cold in the attic. Robby wrapped his blanket around him and watched his breath rise from his mouth into the air. The spring season finally brought some relief. The hard ground thawed and softened. Tulip sprouts burst from the ground. Tiny flowers bloomed on the fruit trees. Green buds dotted the bare bushes along the side of the house. Mothers once again hung their wet wash on their clotheslines.

Robby and his brother and sisters were loaded in the station wagon and driven to Danvers, Massachusetts, to his father's extended family's Easter picnic. At the park, Robby visited his numerous aunts and uncles and cousins. Skinny and lanky, fair-skinned with sky-blue eyes, Robby looked like a foreigner among his father's stockier-built relatives. But he had fun with his numerous cousins, playing croquet, hide and seek, and tag. He avoided his paternal grandparents. His grandmother had proven that she could not be trusted. One time she had visited their house and sat with Robby while he played in his button box. He picked up pieces of a zippo lighter and cleverly showed her how he could put the lighter back together. Then he clicked the lighter, and it ignited, producing a flame. She immediately stood, went to Robby's father in the living room, and told him Robby was playing with fire. His father roared into the kitchen, grabbed Robby by his arm and, backhanded Robby in the face, then swung Robby around like a ragdoll. Robby looked at his grandmother. She smiled, looking as if she enjoyed watching

Robby getting beaten. She had often bragged about how she had hit her own children into submission and was not above throwing sticks or anything she could quickly grab to whip at them. She said if a hand slap did not work, she would use a stick. If that didn't work, she beat them with frying pans. Robby knew not to go near her, so at the picnic, he avoided her. His mother sat quietly in a lawn chair, listening to her in-laws talk, but she seemed disconnected from them and was constantly on the lookout for her children, especially Robby.

But Robby loved running free with other children. He enjoyed the picnic too, the abundant hot dogs and potato salad, the pickles, the homemade cookies and cakes. Best of all, Coca-Cola bottles were in the coolers, and he could drink as much of it as he wanted. In the early afternoon, Darin talked Robby into leaving the picnic with him and hopping onto the subway train.

"We'll have an adventure," Darin said. "We won't be gone long."

Together they ran away from the family, walking the sidewalk and then dropping down the stairs to the subway.

After they rode the subway a few miles, Darin said, "Let's get off here."

They stepped onto a busy city street filled with cars, stores, delicatessens, and adult movie theatres and walked along the sidewalk littered with prostitutes hanging by doors and men walking by. Pornographic posters of women were stamped onto the brick buildings. Robby looked at it all. Sailors hung around the street.

"I don't like it here," Robby said, feeling uneasy. "Let's go back."

"This is the combat zone. Come on." Darin led his younger brother a few blocks along the street. Robby stepped around the paper trash. A disheveled man lay near a doorway.

"Is he dead?" Robby asked.

"No, he's sleeping," Darin said.

At the end of the street, they came to the interstate's entrance and exit ramps. Junk littered the area. Papers flew in the wind. An old tractor sat off to the side. They stepped off the street and onto the open field near Highway 95. Darin suddenly disappeared.

Robby looked around. His brother was gone. "Darin, where are you?" He circled around. He did not see him. A few moments passed. "Darin, this is not funny. Stop playing."

Darin came out from behind the tractor, swinging a large metal pipe, and drove it into the top of Robby's head. Blood burst out, spilling over Robby's face and eyes. He staggered. He tried to retain his balance. His legs wobbled. Within seconds, he dropped hard, slamming his face into the gravel. He turned his face to the side and, from blood-stained vision, saw Darin racing away toward the highway's off-ramp. Robby watched his brother running until he was no longer visible.

Robby lay flat on his stomach. He wanted to get up, but he could not move. His hair was saturated with blood. Blood spilled onto the ground. He lay, dazed. A station wagon drove by and abruptly stopped. Robby heard the car door slam. Robby managed to roll over. A man peered over him. Robby tried to focus on the man.

"You ok?" the man asked. He was dressed in a black suit.

Robby could not respond. What would happen to him now? The man reached his hands under Robby's back, picked him up, and carried him to his car. He opened the back door and lifted Robby onto the lap of three little girls dressed in Easter Sunday pink, white, and blue dresses. Blood flowed from the head wound onto the car seat and onto the girls. They screamed.

"He's bloody," one girl said.

Another girl asked, "Is he going to die?"

"No, he ain't, but I'm getting to Boston General as fast as I can," the man said.

"Are we going to make it to church?" one girl asked.

"God will forgive us if we're late," the mother said.

Robby was more scared than he had ever been. He wondered if he would die. But he was breathing fine. His head hurt.

The man swerved to the right and onto an uphill driveway. He drove to the hospital entrance and stopped. He got out of the car, opened the door, and lifted Robby up into his arms. "Come on, son. You're going to be fine now." He carried Robby into the hospital and walked to the woman at the desk. "You better look at this boy right away. I found him lying near the road. At first, I thought he was dead."

"Who is he?" the woman asked.

"I don't know. He doesn't talk. His head is busted open."

Two nurses came out with a wheelchair. The man put Robby in the chair.

"I'll see you, son," the man said. "Get better now."

Robby was in too much shock to respond.

"Do you know his name?" the receptionist asked the man.

"No," he said. "I made a wrong turn and exited the highway. I saw the kid lying on the side of the ramp. I thought he was dead."

The nurses wheeled Robby through the doors to an emergency room stall. He was lifted onto a bed. Doctors arrived and assessed Robby's injuries.

"What happened to you, son?" a grey-haired doctor asked. He lightly touched the top of Robby's head and groaned. "Ouch. That must hurt."

Robby shook. Dizziness and nausea gripped him. The room was spun. He remained mute. He was afraid of what his father would do to him once he found him at the hospital, so he decided it was best not to talk at all. He was in terrible pain and cried out when the doctor pulled up his shirt and exposed his chest. Bruises were exposed. His rib-bones protruded. He was sent for X-rays and told to lay still as other tests involving big machines were conducted. Blood tests were taken, and a needle with a tube attached was inserted in the top of his hand that fed him liquids from a bag. Robby lay passive and expressionless. But he was grateful for the care. The doctor told him he suffered a head injury, which they were going to have to watch for a few days. They sewed up the huge gash in his head, then wrapped it in bandages.

He was taken to a room and put in another bed. He moved in and out of deep sleep. His ears produced a continuous ringing sound that distorted his ability to hear.

His vision blurred. The nurses came in often and tried to get him to talk, but Robby remained silent. If he revealed who he was, his father would arrive and drag him back to the attic. The hospital staff took a photo of him in bed, his head bandaged, and his face swollen. Robby felt defeated. He lacked the energy to respond.

A nurse came into the room on the third day. She gave him a sip of water from a straw. "You are in the Boston newspaper and on the television news. The media is doing what it can to find out who you belong to."

Robby lay still. He hoped his family would never find him.

On the third day, he heard his father talking to the nurses at the station just outside his door. "That's my son you have."

He heard a woman say. "Your son was brought in here by a stranger who found him beaten on the side of a road. We searched for you everywhere. Your son was on the front page of the newspaper and on the local television news. Why did it take you three days to get here?"

His Father's authoritarian voice boomed. "I did not know where he was. I left him in the care of relatives. He ran away. He's wayward! A complete delinquent. How was I to know? He does not listen. He takes off whenever he wants to."

His father charged into the room and looked at Robby. "Get dressed. We are going home."

Robby was dressed in his T-shirt and shorts, still stained with dried blood. He followed his father out the door. Instead of showing fear, Robby appeared recalcitrant. He didn't challenge his father, but inside he felt defiant and angry. He followed his father out the door and into the car. No one stopped them. When they returned home, Robby climbed the stairs and went into the attic.

The next morning, his sister gave his attic door her special knock. After a few minutes, he opened the door, grabbed the bowl of oatmeal, shut the door, and locked it. He quickly ate the oatmeal. Downstairs, the house was eerily quiet. No one was talking. No one did that the entire day.

CHAPTER 13

After the hospital stay, Robby was permitted to eat dinner with the family for a few nights, but he was denied the regular family meal and was given a liverwurst sandwich, but his stomach ached for the beef stroganoff dripping over thick noodles that the rest of the family was feasting on. After his siblings finished eating, Robby was allowed to eat the scraps of his siblings' plates, which were collectively meager and not enough to fill his hunger. Then Robby scurried to the attic and bolted the door shut.

Robby lived by his own rules. His family was unaware that he was spending less time locked in the attic. If the attic was hot, he left the house through the cellar door and slept in the willow tree behind his house. He made a bed of leaves in the groove of two large branches. At dawn, he grabbed onto a branch that lowered him to the ground and snuck back into the attic without anyone knowing. Some days he walked to the millpond and slept on his platform. He loved watching the stars and the airplanes fly by.

His father's weekend dumps in the city of Boston on his way to the Red Sox games turned out to be a good lesson for Robby. Soon after he was abandoned, he waited until his father's car had disappeared and then hurried to the train tracks. Once a slow-moving train's flat car became visible, he grabbed its metal bars, lifted his feet up, pulled his body onto the flatbed, and rode the rails to the mill ponds. Sitting on his homemade platform high in the trees, he felt powerful and strong. The mill pond was his sanctuary, his secret refuge, a place where he felt completely safe, a place just for him. No one knew where he was. He was as free as the birds he grew to love and admire. They flew around the trees, whistling and chattering. Robby imitated their calls. Other times he lay still and quiet, waiting for the birds to land near him. When they did, he marveled at their beauty. He watched them as they paired up, the plain females with the colorful males. For hours, he watched the mated birds collect sticks and leaves for their nests. After they laid their eggs, he was careful not to disturb them. He saw hawks swoop down and steal some of the eggs before they hatched. Remembering Uncle Irving's lesson that what he saw happen in nature was meant to be, he did not react, but he still felt sorry for the mated birds who lost their offspring. But when other eggs hatched, he watched the helpless hatchlings ask for food, their mouths wide open. Their parents carefully brought them worms to eat. At night, Robby watched the owls fly above the trees. The insects were invited to share his platform, and he slept like a baby in the bosom of the trees.

In the field, he picked a handful of wildflowers to give to his mother. He carried them to the house to give them to her, but when he saw his father's truck in the driveway, he stopped. He stared at the house for a while and finally threw the flowers on the ground and walked back to his platform house.

Kids knew to stay far away from the Begin home. The neighbors nicknamed his father mayhem-Charley. But Robby was accepted by his peers. They often took him home to eat with their families. It did not take the parents long to notice that Mayhem- Charley was abusing Robby. Because of his obvious mistreatment, the town's mothers not only fed Robby but also kept him for the night. When he awoke in the morning, his clothes were washed, mended, and folded nicely into a neat pile. For the first time in his life, Robby was learning that there were kind people in the world like his Aunt May and Uncle Irving and that he was well-liked in the community, if only because people felt sorry for him.

He gained personal freedom that none of his friends or any child his age had. He was liberated and free to live his life the way he wanted to. But his new teacher was not so fond of Robby's lack of concentration when it came to doing his classwork. She realized she could control Robby's behavior by contacting his father to complain about him. One day, Robby's father showed up to the classroom unannounced, marched to Robby, grabbed his arm, pulled him up, and proceeded to slap him across his face.

The teacher ran to Robby and pulled him away from his father. "Leave now, Mr. Begin," she ordered. She pulled Robby into the fold of her dress and held him.

The other children left their seats and ran from the room. Robby hid in his teacher's loose dress, not so much embarrassed as petrified. His father stormed from the room, marched down the school corridor, and out the door. The school principal banned his father from ever stepping foot in the school again.

When the teacher saw Robby was not completing his assignments, she called him to her desk after school let out one day. "Robby, from now on, you are not required to do your homework. I will grade you solely on your classroom work." From then on, Robby made every effort to correctly complete his classroom work, and his grades went from /C/s to /B/s.

One day, he played a prank on his mother as she made dinner in the kitchen. He sat at the table, thumbing through his button box. He found a large rubber band and thought it would be funny to shoot it at his mom, so he did. As soon as he released the rubber band, he knew he had made a mistake. The rubber band made a snapping sound when it hit her leg. She jumped and screamed. She whipped around and hit him with a dishcloth. He immediately felt betrayed by her. She was always the one who looked out for him. She was the only one who really cared for him. But quickly he felt ashamed. He had hurt his mother, the only person who loved him. A ball of confusion raced through him. In that instant, he knew he had to get out of his God-forsaken misery. He stood, ran out the door, and raced down the block toward the police station. This was the final insult, and he knew he needed help. He ran to the door and opened it. He asked the man at the front desk to talk to a police officer. The man led Robby into an office where a police officer sat at a desk.

Bravely, Robby said, "I need help. My father hits me."

"Now, son," the police officer said, looking skeptical.

"Don't make me go home," Robby begged. But suddenly, he realized the police officer was not going to help him.

"Give me your name and address, son," the police officer said.

Robby turned to leave. What had he been thinking?

"There now, son." The police officer said. "Just let me help you out. I cannot help you without knowing who you are or where you live."

Reluctantly, Robby gave him his name and address. The police officer brought him some Coca-Cola and a candy bar. He let him sit beside him at his desk. And then the help that he so needed was thwarted when his father showed up at the office. His father rushed inside, full of anger and vengeance. When he saw Robby sitting in a nice, comfortable chair, sipping Coca-Cola, he angrily went to him, picked him up by his collar, and backhanded Robby so hard in his face that he flew back and landed on the policeman's desk, pushing the policeman's prized, name-engraved plaque with the title, Chief-of-Police off the desk.

"How dare you accuse me of treating you badly," his father yelled to Robby. Then he turned to the officer. "Officer, this boy is wayward, incorrigible. He lies all the time. I cannot control what he says or does. I am sorry for your trouble."

"You're going to have to get him under control," the police officer told his father.

As his father picked Robby up by his ear and dragged him out of the office and out the door, Robby kept his eyes on the officer, silently pleading for his help. His father threw Robby into the car, started the motor, and drove him home. Once at home, Robby ran to the attic and locked himself inside it. Safe, he lay on his bed defeated. He was alone and always would be. He had no home. No one would rescue him.

CHAPTER 14

A heavy snowfall blanketed the town. Robby's mother said he could go sledding with Darin down the hill that was located a few blocks from their house. She gave Robby a warm coat and some mittens to wear, and he and Darin walked to the hill, each with a sled.

The hill was a tall dirt mound created from leftover dirt from a nearby new housing development. When it was covered in snow, all the neighborhood children sledded down it, but today only Robby, Darin, and Johnny from a few blocks down went there to sled. The three boys spent the afternoon sledding. They raced down the hill with gusto. At the bottom of the hill was an average-sized maple tree. To keep from crashing into the tree, the boys made two paths for their sleds to navigate around either side of the tree. The snow became very compact and icy as the day progressed, giving the boys a thrilling ride each time.

Johnny ran to the top, sat on the sled, and pushed himself down the hill. He went so fast that he could not turn away from the tree and crashed into the base of a trunk. He tumbled over and lay on his side in the snow. Robby thought he was playing and would get up, so he ran up the hill and sledded down one more time. He noticed Johnny was not moving, so he went over to him. Johnny looked like he was sleeping. Darin approached him. Robby shook Johnny, but he did not respond.

"We should take him home," Robby said to Darin.

"No, he's fine," Darin said and turned away.

Robby stared at Johnny. "He's sleeping."

"Just leave him," Darin said. "He'll wake up."

"No," Robby refused. He touched Johnny's skin. He was becoming cold. With effort, he lifted Johnny onto his sled and began to pull him toward his home.

Darin came along, but when they reached their block, Darin said, "I'm cold. I'm going home." Darin ran toward home, pulling his sled behind him.

Robby was cold too, but he was also worried about Johnny. He continued to pull Johnny as fast as he could, but Johnny was heavier than him. Robby navigated carefully. Several times Johnny fell off the sled, and Robby put him back on. He pulled him past the other blocks. When he finally reached Johnny's house, he pulled him up to the doorway and rang the doorbell.

Johnny's father answered. When he saw his son lying still on the sled with Robby holding his rope, he hurried to his son. "What happened?"

"My brother and I were sledding with him. He sledded down Marshall Hill and hit a tree. Then he fell asleep. I could not wake him. He is getting cold. He needs to be warmed up."

His father called his wife to call an ambulance. Robby noticed he was the same police officer who had called his father when Robby had gone to the station to get help for himself. It suddenly dawned on Robby that Johnny was the Chief-of-Police's son. The officer picked up his son and carried him into the house.

Robby turned to walk home. When he was two blocks down the road, he heard the ambulance. He kept walking and did not look back. When he arrived home, he went straight to his attic and stayed until school started again a few days later. It was there that he learned that Johnny had died.

He was incredibly sad, but he kept his sadness to himself. He thought Johnny had just been sleeping. How did he die? He wanted to know, but he did not think he should speak about it. So, he did not ask.

Darin needed help with his paper route for two weeks when a winter storm gripped New England, so Robby pitched in to help. With the money Robby earned, he decided to buy Christmas presents for the entire family. He ran to the local five-and-dime store and the grocery store to pick out the gifts. He bought a Mickey Spillane book from a rack at the grocery store for his mother. He bought a pack of number 2 pencils for Terry. He purchased a gum pack for Nancy. He bought a baseball card for Darin and a pen for his father. He bought a rattle for his baby sister, Alice. In the attic, he wrapped the presents with leftover newspaper and put them in the corner to wait for the holiday.

On Christmas morning, Robby awoke in the cold attic. He climbed out of his bed and quickly dressed. He got the presents and put them on the floor by the door. A wave of happiness washed over him. He could not wait to see how excited his family would be to receive his gifts. He rinsed his face and hands in the sink and dressed in a shirt and pants. Then he sat by the attic window and watched his neighbors leave their houses and drive down the street. Light snow fell, blanketing the neighborhood with enough flurries to cover the lawns and streets and parked cars.

After a while, his mother called up the attic stairs. "Robby, come to breakfast. It's Christmas morning." Her voice was cheerful and enthusiastic.

Robby grabbed the presents and bundled them into the fold of one arm. With his other hand, he unlatched his door and then climbed down the narrow, creaking steps. Once he stepped into the kitchen, he saw his entire family sitting at the breakfast table. Bacon, scrambled eggs, toast, and orange juice were ready to be served. Robby went into the living room area and put his presents by the Christmas tree. The tree lights shimmered above the numerous presents beneath it. For a moment, he admired it and then went into the kitchen and took his place at the kitchen table. His older sisters, his brother, and his baby sister, were sitting silent and still, so he did too. He did not look at his father.

"You may say the grace for us, Robby," his mother said.

Robby folded his hands and closed his eyes. "Dear Lord, Bless this food that you have bestowed upon us to nourish our bodies. We thank you for your love and kindness on this holy day, the blessed day of your birth. On this Christmas day, may we cherish and remember the generous gift you have given us of eternal life. Amen." He opened his eyes, unfolded his hands, and put them in his lap. He looked at his mother, whose eyes were locked on his and glistening with tears.

"You have such a way with words," she told Robby.

Robby remained silent. He had been attending the town's Catholic church as often as he could. He had learned the eloquence of prayers and their meaning by listening to the priests. But for now, he focused on the food and his siblings surrounding him. He copied their lead by staying still and quiet. Their father, a modest-looking man, loomed large at the head of the table. His mother passed the food around the table. Robby was careful to only place on his plate the amount his siblings placed. Then they all ate breakfast together. No one talked much during the meal. Robby was careful not to make a sound, not to clang his fork on the plate or set his orange juice cup too hard on the table after taking a sip.

Afterward, they went to the living room to open the presents. They all gathered around the Christmas tree. His sisters smiled. They eagerly awaited their presents. Robby was especially looking forward to giving his family the gifts he bought them.

"Robby, hand each of your sisters and your brother your presents," his mother said to him.

Robby picked up his presents and, one by one, handed each family member their gift. They all opened their gifts together, ripping off the scraps of newspaper. When they saw what he had given him, they at first looked perplexed.

Darin laughed. "This is just a silly baseball card."

"Pencils," Terry said, then laughed along with her siblings.

Robby wanted to say that he had given her the pencils to thank him for the paper and pencils she had given him, but he remained silent.

"You gave us cheap gumball toys," Darin said and dropped his baseball card on the floor.

His sisters laughed. His father looked at Robby with contempt. He dropped his pen on the floor. Robby was hurt and humiliated by their criticism. He had delivered newspapers in a blizzard and then spent all the money he received to buy them each a gift. Somewhere in the deep core of his beliefs, he thought that if he persevered through the storm and bought something for all of them that they would truly accept him into the fold of the family, but here they were, laughing at him, mocking him for his kind gesture. This hurt him more than Darin hitting him on the head with hammers or his father smashing his head into the wall. He did not understand what was so funny about the gifts he had given them. He looked at his mother, who was clutching her Mickey Spillane book to her chest, looking embarrassed for Robby.

His mother said, "Robby, can you pass the rest of the presents around to everyone?"

Robby regrouped, shook off his feelings, and followed his mom's lead. He suddenly felt privileged to be given the responsibility of giving each sibling their gift. He took his job seriously and carefully gave each one their gifts. The entire family watched each sibling open them one by one. There were dolls, new clothes, and an electric racetrack and racecar set for Darin.

"You are not allowed to ever touch that racecar set," Robby's father said to Robby, looking at him with contempt.

A wave of sadness overcame Robby. Of course, he would not be allowed to touch it. He was never allowed to touch any toy Darin had received over the years, including the electric train set Darin had received the year before. He listened as Darin and each sister smiled and thanked their parents.

Family photos were taken. Robby stood at the edge of the family, looking at the floor, feeling sadder than he had ever felt before. The photo was shot, and then his siblings gathered up their gifts and ran to their bedrooms. His parents retreated to the kitchen, leaving Robby alone with his own gifts. He was bewildered that they left before he opened his. But then he looked at the wrapped presents that were labelled for him and thought at least he had received gifts. He opened one of his boxes. It was empty. He opened another one. It was empty too. He opened five boxes to find them all empty. Heartbroken, he grabbed the empty boxes and torn wrapping paper and ran to the attic and locked himself inside.

He lit his candle and placed it on his chair. He put on his paper pirate hat and picked up his cardboard sword. Standing on the wall was his shadow friend, his best friend, who would never hurt him. They sparred together for an hour until warmth once again filled his body, his cheeks flushed with renewed energy. Then he blew out the candle and stared out the window at the frosty winter closing in on him. His despair deepened. For the first time in a long time, he thought he may not survive. His father's blows had not hurt him. The police officer had not hurt him. But at that moment, he was injured beyond repair.

Later, Nancy knocked on his door. He was not hungry, but he finally got up and walked to the door and opened it. There was a plate with the collection of his siblings' Christmas dinner food scraps all mixed on the plate. He picked it up and put the plate on his small table, and then went back to bed. Without heat, the room was unbearably cold. He pulled his blanket over his head and hid.

A week later, while his father was at work, he joined the family downstairs. His sisters played in their bedroom. Darin, his brother, was in his bedroom too. Robby sat at the kitchen table while his mother baked a pie in the kitchen. He quietly played with the screws and nuts, and thread in his button box. His mother gave him a liverwurst sandwich and some milk. He gobbled it down. His mother sang along to her Mario Lanza records. Occasionally, she turned to him, wrung her hands in her apron, and looked at Robby with a worried expression. Robby knew better than to talk. After a while, he got up and went into the living room. The Christmas tree was still up, and the lights were turned on. Glass bulbs and shimmering tinsel brightened the tree. Robby sat on the floor and looked at the tree. He could no longer see the beauty in it. If he had his way, trees would not be cut down to display in people's houses during the Christmas holidays. He loved the trees in nature. He loved to climb them and watch the way the wind wrestled the leaves and branches. He loved the hemlock trees in Nova Scotia, the way they dotted the rolling land that stretched in every direction. A Christmas tree was a tree cut and destroyed, made to be displayed unnaturally for selfish humans.

He saw a photo album sitting on a table beside a chair. He opened it and looked at the family photos. He saw the recent photos of their family Christmas. He was in the photos near the tree, but he was shocked to see that someone had taken a black marker and colored him completely out of the photos. He turned the pages. In more photos, he had been blackened out. He had been completely erased from the family. His Father said he would never amount to much, and that he did not belong in the family. He claimed Robby was not his son. Darin often said of Robby, "He marches to a different drummer." He repeated it often. Mortified, Robby shut the album, ran into the kitchen, picked up his button box, and scurried back up to the attic.

In the dark attic, Robby was anxious and restless. He could not sit on the mattress or the little chair. He paced around the attic, shaking his arms. The loose floorboards wobbled under his feet. Then his eyes fell on the empty boxes and wrapping paper, his only Christmas present. An idea came to him. He could make his own shadow puppet-theatre out of the boxes and paper. With the new theatre, he would no longer have to use the candle-illuminated wall to tell his stories with his paper puppets. He sat down on the floor and designed his theatre sections with a pencil on the cardboard. He cut the cardboard pieces out and designed a stage floor and a back and sides. At the top, he inserted a long stick that stretched across the top of the theatre, then attached wrapping-paper curtains through the stick that could open and shut. He cut out an elaborate crown for the top of the stage to make it look grand and pleasing to look at. With more cardboard, he made props – streetlights, benches, beds, dressers, and a sofa. He used cardboard to make adults, children, elephants, cows, dogs, and cats, lions, monkeys, horses, and little rabbits. He colored them with his crayons. He attached the figurines to long sticks that he would use to control each puppet from the top of the stage. Then he made trees and bushes. When he was done, he set up the stage and got his characters ready. He lit his candle and set it on the chair. The theatre magically illuminated. He imagined a grand stage, people filing in to watch the show. The actors were ready. He placed the trees and bushes on the stage. And then he began the play. Stories flowed from his imagination. Each character had its own personality. Good characters fought evil characters. The good always won. In his mind, Robby floated between fantasy and the real world, from the city where he lived to the Nova Scotia farm where he had earned his new identity as a great explorer. Hope lived inside each story. Heroes won each battle. Animals became real and took care of each other, comforted each other, and comforted Robby. He was the king of the puppet stories. Most of all, with all his puppets, he was not alone.

CHAPTER 15

The next year at Christmas time, Robby drew large pictures of the gifts he had given his family the year before. He drew a book for his mom, a pen for his father, a baseball card for Darin, pencils for Terry, and a gum pack for Nancy. He colored the pictures and then taped them to a piece of plywood he had taken from his father's woodshop. On Christmas Eve, after everyone was asleep, he carried the plywood into the living room and set the plywood against the tree. Then he ran back to the attic, where he lay under a blanket, cold and alone. In the morning, he did not join his family for their breakfast, gift-giving celebration, or dinner. He lay alone on the mattress in the dark attic, listening to his family laughing and enjoying the holiday together. Each breath he took sent a cloudy vapor above his face. He tried to warm up by wrapping his body in his blanket, but he was unsuccessful. The cold and snow prevented him from going to the mill ponds to focus on his own life, but he closed his eyes and imagined it. He soared over it, the trees, the streams, the platform house. As he flew, he felt some comfort. He promised himself he would never celebrate a holiday again.

That summer, Darin joined the local Riverside Little League team to play baseball. The team's coach suddenly quit, citing family and work issues. Robby's father volunteered to coach the team. In the evening, to prepare for the games, he took Darin to the front yard and taught him how to throw the ball and catch it in the mitt. Robby sat on the porch steps and watched his father work with his brother. He was not permitted to join in. But when the season started, the team was short players, so his father put Robby in a uniform and parked him on the bench so he would have the required number of players on the bench for the team to be allowed to play each game. But after two games, one team member did not show up for the game. Robby's dad had no choice but to put Robby up to bat. Robby had never hit the ball before and did not know any of the rules of the game. He had never practiced with the team. During games, he sat on the bench, shuffling his feet through the powdery dirt, daydreaming about fishing and hanging out in his tree house.

At the plate, Robby took the bat and prepared his proper stance. He held the bat in the position he had seen the other team players do. When the ball was pitched to him, he swung. The ball launched far upward between first and second base and almost went out of the park. Robby stood for a moment and watched the ball fly away. Then, looking at the location of the ball, which was closer to first base than third base, Robby made the strategic decision to run to third base instead of first base, thinking he had more of a chance to reach it. He dropped the bat and ran toward third base. He reached third base and decided to run toward second base. The crowd cheered wildly. Robby was elated. Someone caught the ball and threw it toward second base, but Robby rounded the corner and, cruising sideways, headed toward first base. Above the roar of the crowd, Robby heard his father and teammates cheering him on. This was Robby's chance to finally please his father. For the first time he had done something right in his father's eyes. Robby raced toward first base, electrified with excitement, bubbling with joy. The first baseman fumbled the ball. Robby tagged first base and headed toward home plate. His father jumped, shouting his encouragement. Finally, his father would be proud of him. A burst of pride filled Robby. He was achieving a monumental victory. For once, he would be the hero. But when he reached home plate and tried to touch it, his father leaned into him and punched him so hard in the face that his feet slipped out from under him. Robby's arms flailed. Upward he flew. He kicked his legs. His back slammed into the ground. His head pounded into the dirt. Shocked and stunned, he lay motionless. Soot floated in a cloud around him. He did not move or touch his injured face, but he felt the blood running down it. He stared upward at the sky.

Finally, he got up. People walked past him. The game was over. The kids laughed at him. "You ran the wrong way."

Robby looked around. What? The wrong way?

"Stupid idiot," one player told him.

Embarrassed and humiliated, Robby reached his hand to his face and touched the blood. Everyone was leaving. They gathered their water jugs, their sweaters off the spectators' benches and walked toward their parked cars. Robby staggered to the end of the ball field. If only his mother had been there, but she was home cooking the winning celebration dinner of hamburgers, french fries, fresh tomatoes, and potato salad. There would be an apple pie for dessert.

Another father walked up to Robby and pulled Robby into the fold of his chest, and hugged him.

Robby's father shouted. "What are you doing? Do not touch my boy. Mind your own business."

The father shouted to Robby's father. "You are wrong. You are wrong. You are wrong!"

"Don't touch my kid," Robby's father said.

The man released Robby, patted him on the back, and walked away. Robby left the ballpark and walked along the road, passing the families leaving in their cars. His father was taking the team out for ice cream, but he was not invited. Robby walked home and went straight to the attic.

Later that day, while the family was enjoying the family barbecue, he walked to mill ponds. He disappeared into the tangle of trees and branches, becoming invisible, and walked until he reached his tree. He climbed the tree, stepped onto his platform home, and sank onto his bed of pine needles and leaves. He lay, staring at the sky. He reached his hand to his injured nose and set it straight. Then he watched the nightfall, the stars gathering in the sky in a brilliant display. Comforted by the night sky, he fell into a merciful sleep. In his dream, he traveled to the great Nova Scotia land, where he became the great explorer of the massive Canadian land, free to roam the great countryside, engulfed in the land that understood and cared for him. In his dream, he jumped on Uncle Irving's massive, white horse and raced along the open land ensconced in nature's bountiful gifts, the trees, the blue sky, the warm sun, the bears, the rivers, the fish, the birds. He had nothing left to fear.

He awoke before dawn to raindrops pelting his face and the pit of his stomach hollow with hunger. He climbed down the tree and slipped along the forest until he reached the stream. There, long before the day began, he caught six fish with his hands. He put some of the wiggling fish in his baseball cap and carried them to his tree, and climbed up to his platform. He took his knife and cleaned the fish. He ate the fish raw, feeling some relief from his hunger.

The rain increased, so he moved to the end of his platform that was canopied by tree branches. He stayed there for the day, crouched under the thick branches and leaves that protected him from the rain. Throughout the day, he fantasized about being in Nova Scotia with his uncle and aunt, imagined eating her delicious meals, and helping his uncle cultivate the crops. He imagined what help he would be to his aunt May in their little store attached to the house, the friendly greetings he would receive from the neighbors who came to trade goods. He wanted to go to them, but he had no way to get there. For now, he was safe. His nose was in the right place, the swelling on his face was diminishing, and he could not see the bruises.

He waited until the end of the day to go back home. He stealthily snuck into the basement through the cellar door, tiptoed along his father's wood shop, and climbed up the back of the stairs into the attic. He collapsed on his bed and slept for another day.

Robby's father was the most skilled furniture and cabinet maker on the northern east coast and was in high demand for his services. He spent most of his free time filling orders from people who wanted his built-in kitchen cabinets and his hand-crafted furniture. To complete each project, he required Robby's presence in the room to clean up after him while he worked. Since they did not have a normal father-son relationship, no words were spoken between them, only gestures that revealed his father's demands and expectations. But Robby was observant. He watched his Father work. He had one eye on cleaning the dust and one eye on watching his father feed the wood through the saws. Sometimes, Robby snuck into the cellar and hid under the old furniture in the corner to watch his dad work on his orders. How he loved the buzzing sound the saws made, the way the saws precisely cut the wood. On the days Robby's father had gone to his day job at the chemical plant, Robby went into his cellar workshop and looked at the big saws. After watching his father use them, he felt confident he could use them too.

Robby walked by the small music store in town. He liked the guitars he saw hanging in the front window. He wished he could have one, but he did not feel comfortable going into the store to look at them. He loitered in front of the store, pacing back and forth, wishing he had one of the magnificent guitars. After a while, he got an idea. He would make his own guitar using his father's saws.

While his father was at work, he discreetly went into his father's shop and found a large piece of discarded plywood in the corner. On it, he drew the shape of a guitar body, then the neck, copying the look of the acoustic guitars he saw hanging in the music shop window. He turned on the saw and, trying to match his father's accurate skill, slowly cut out the body, then the neck, then the top. When he was done, he turned off the saw, laid his new guitar down, and cleaned the area around the shop so his father would never know he had used his saw and plywood. He brought the guitar into the attic and carefully trimmed and smoothed out the edges. He had a perfectly shaped, flat guitar, which he believed he could play.

But to play it, he needed strings. He took it to the music shop and went inside. He walked to the two men standing behind the counter. Robby proudly laid his guitar on the countertop. "Can you put strings on my guitar so I can play it," he asked them.

The men looked at Robby's flat, plywood guitar, then at Robby. The men looked at each other. One raised his eyebrow. They both looked surprised and a bit bewildered. One scratched his chin. They looked back at Robby, then at his guitar, then back at each other. They were quiet for a moment. They nodded their heads as if agreeing on something.

One of them looked at Robby. "This is your guitar?"

"Yes," Robby said.

"Can I see it?"

"Sure." Robby was eager to show off his first guitar.

The man held it up and looked at it. "Where you'd get this?"

"I made it."

"You did?" He picked it up, turned it over, and looked at the edges. "Good job. You want to learn to play?"

"Yes," Robby said.

The man put the guitar back on the counter. The two men glanced at each other and smiled. Then they both looked back at Robby with sympathetic expressions. Robby immediately sensed they were going to help him.

"Well, you need a real guitar like the ones hanging on the wall over there." The man pointed to the row of guitars hanging from the ceiling. There was a shiny, black grand piano nearby.

Disappointment filled Robby. He could never afford one of those guitars. His shoulders slumped.

"I'll tell you what," the man said. "What's your name?"

"Robby."

He leaned in toward Robby, stooping to his level. He smiled. "Robby, you come here on Saturdays and help me wipe the fingerprints off the guitars, violins, cellos and clean a little bit around here. If you do that, I'll help you out with a guitar."

Robby perked up. "Ok."

"You just come on by and do a good job. No fooling around. Just polishing. Is that a deal?"

"I'll be here."

"I will see you then," the man said.

"Ok, thanks." Robby took his flat guitar and left. All the way home he skipped.

The next Saturday he showed up at the music store and polished all the guitars, the electric keyboards, and the drums, being careful to remove every fingerprint and smudge. He took special care polishing the grand piano. He knew from working in his father's shop that he had to be quick, efficient, and silent. He was an expert at cleaning and being invisible. When he touched the back of a cello, one of its strings vibrated. He put his ear against the dark wood to listen to it, marveling at the rich sound it made. He rubbed the cloth against it, listening to the soft vibration that came from the inside. He knew not to touch the strings but just wiping the wood gave him such a pleasant sensation that he fell in love with not only the cello but all the instruments in the store. With his gentle stroke, he wiped the instruments until the wood on each one glowed. Side by side, hanging from the ceiling, along the wall, they looked magnificent.

When Robby was done, the store owner gave him 50 cents. "I am Joe Rossi, by the way. The next time you come, I will have a guitar for you."

The next Saturday, Robby went to the music shop to polish all the instruments. When he finished, Bobby Harrison walked out of the back room with an acoustic guitar.

"Here's your new guitar." Bobby handed it to Robby.

Once the guitar was in his hands, Robby smiled. He did not know what to say. He held it securely in his hands, feeling an overflowing feeling of happiness and gratitude.

"Here, kid," Bobby said. "Let me show you how to use it." He took the guitar back. "Sit down on the chair."

Robby sat down. For the next hour, Bobby taught him how the guitar worked. He showed him how to tune it, how to hold his fingers on the fretboard, and how to strum the strings at the base. "You come by every Saturday, polish my instruments, and I'll give you a lesson." He smiled. "Deal?"

"I will."

"Now you go enjoy your new guitar. I have other work to do," Bobby said.

Robby proudly carried it home and took it to the attic. He sat down and tried to play it. It did not sound right, so he fiddled with the tunings. When it sounded like something that resembled a chord, he strummed it. He was used to figuring things out on his own, and he approached the instrument with his own unique style. He had made many gadgets from his button box and never grew tired of inventing new things to play with and visually admire. But to him, the guitar was not just another gadget for him to play with. The sound he made reverberated like magic to his ears. For the first time in his life, he found something he really connected to. The guitar was not just something he could fiddle with or admire. He could express what he was feeling and experiencing in his life. Quickly, in the first two weeks after he received the guitar, he felt he had found something that could change him.

He went to the music store every Saturday and cleaned the entire store. He found out Joe Rossi was part of the Bobby Harrison Trio, and they played all over the east coast. The group ran the music store. They were pleased with Robby's work and did their part by giving him guitar lessons for free.

Every day in the attic, Robby worked on creating his own songs on the guitar. He got better and better. One day, though, after he had cleaned the cellar, he absentmindedly left his guitar there and went to the attic. He locked the door and sat on the chair, looking around at the bare, dark walls.

His father banged on the attic door. "Robby, open up now!"

Fear raced through Robby. He knew by the tone in his father's voice that he was in danger. More hunger, more bruises, and, worst of all, humiliation would ensue when he opened the door. His Father was a monstrous force he was unable to stop. The best he could do was stay quiet and hide. He ran to the corner, sat down, and hid, wrapping his long, thin legs to his chest. But his father was persistent, and eventually, Robby unlocked the door and faced his father.

"Where'd you get this?" his father shouted, shoving the guitar at Robby.

"At the music shop down the street." Robby stiffened, waiting to be slapped. But instead, his father turned and marched down the stairs and left the house carrying Robby's guitar. Robby watched him get into his car, throw his guitar on the backseat, and drive off. Robby could not stand the thought of losing his guitar. He charged outside and dashed to the music store. His father's car was parked in front of the store. Robby ran to the large front window where all the beautiful guitars hung from ceiling hooks. He peeked into the window and saw his father angrily waving his guitar at Joe Rossi.

"What are you doing giving my son a guitar?" his father shouted at Joe.

Robby cringed. He felt the air go out of him. He thought he would collapse.

"You have no right to do anything with my son unless I say you can," his father continued.

Robby could not see his father's face, but he knew his expression. His eyes were filled with rage. His nostrils flared, his cheeks flushed. Robby sucked in his breath waiting to see what would happen. More than anything he wanted to work at the music store. He wanted the lessons. He wanted their friendship. As he listened to his father's verbal attack, Robby felt himself shrinking, his legs giving out. But then the two other members of the Bobby Harrison Trio came out from the back room and walked behind the counter. The three of them formed a fortress line and faced his father.

Joe grabbed Robby's guitar from his father and handed it to Bobby. He pointed his finger at his father and shouted back at him. "Your son comes here and cleans our shop for us. I gave this guitar to him. He earned it. It's his. If you know what is good for you, you will leave right now and get the hell out of my shop and don't come back." He leaned forward, and waved his fist at Robby's father, who looked small and meek next to the guitar shop owner and the other men. Robby's father turned and headed toward the door. Robby ran to the side of the building and watched his father get into his car and drive home. Robby ran to the railroad tracks and followed the tracks to the mill ponds. He climbed to his treehouse and hid for the rest of the day.

The next day he went to the music store and cleaned it. Joe gave him his guitar back. "Keep this guitar far from your old man. You have one mean son-of-a-bitch father." He gave Robby fifty cents.

Robby walked out the door and went next door to the pet shop. He had often looked in the window and wished for a pet of his own. Hoping fifty cents would be enough, he went inside and walked around. The man behind the counter watched him. Robby saw the mice were only fifty cents apiece. He bought one and brought it home. He found a cardboard box in his Father's shop and brought it up to the attic. Now he had a pet to keep him company. He put the box next to his bed, put the mouse in it, and lay on his bed and watched his new mouse until dusk fell and the night closed in around him. With the mouse, he did not feel so alone. Just his presence comforted him. As he rested in the dark, he listened to his mouse scratching at the box. He fell asleep feeling satisfied with himself that he at least had a pet now.

In the late morning, when he awoke, he looked in the box. The mouse was not there. He lifted the box and saw the mouse had chewed a hole through the corner of it and escaped. Robby searched all around the attic for it. He lifted his desk and looked under it but did not see it. When he placed the desk leg down on the floor, he heard a slight squeak. He lifted the desk and looked under it. His heart sank. He had dropped the leg onto the mouse. He hurt his new friend. He placed the desk back down and picked up the mouse. It was not moving. In a panic, he put the mouse in his pocket and ran to his secret exit at the back of the stairs. Quickly, he descended the back of the steps and ran across his father's workshop and out the cellar door. Running at top speed, he cradled his injured mouse. He sprinted past the corner store, the music shop, and into the pet store.

He hurried to the man behind the counter. "My mouse!" He held it out to the pet shop owner.

The man took his mouse and looked at it. "What did you do to it, kid? You crushed it. It's dead."

"I didn't crush it," Robby cried. "He's not dead. He's hurt."

"He's dead. You killed it."

"I did not! I did not!" Robby cried deep sobs.

Joe, from the music store, came into the pet shop and walked over to Robby. "What happened? I saw you run by my shop, crying."

"Joe! My mouse!" Robby said.

"He killed his fucking mouse," the pet shop owner said to Joe. "I sold him the mouse, and he crushed it."

"I did not!" Robby insisted.

Joe looked at the mouse and then looked at the pet shop owner. "Give the kid another mouse."

"He killed this one. Why should I give him another one?"

"Cause I say so," Joe demanded. He reached into his pocket and threw a bunch of dollar bills on the counter. "Give the kid another mouse. In fact, give him that fancy mouse cage too." He pointed to a large hamster house with a spinning wheel. "And some of that sawdust. You mean to tell me you gave the kid a mouse, but you didn't give him a proper cage to keep the fucking mouse in."

The pet shop owner threw up his hands. "Okay. You got it." He got the cage, filled the bottom of it with sawdust, and then got another live mouse for him.

"Give him a couple of mice," Joe said. "No mouse should be alone."

The man put three mice in the cage and the gave the cage to Robby. He and Joe walked out the door.

"You all right, kid?" Joe asked him.

"Yes," Robby said, cradling his elaborate mouse cage.

Joe patted the back of his head. "Don't you worry about a thing, Robby? When you're in trouble. You come straight to me. You hear?"

"Yes." He stopped crying.

"Now you go home and keep that mouse cage away from your old man," Joe said.

Robby proudly carried his new cage and three new mice home. He walked through the back door into the kitchen, where his mother was making the midday meal.

His mother turned to him. "Well, what do you have, Robby?" She smiled.

"The pet shop gave me this." Robby proudly held up his new mouse house for his mother to see.

"Put it on the table so I can have a look," she said.

Robby placed it on the table and showed his mother the mice scurrying around the cage. They spent time watching them and thinking of names. His mother patted him on his head. She wiped her hands in her apron.

His Father came into the room and stood still for a moment, looking at them both.

"Looky, here, Charles," his mother said cheerfully. "The local pet store gave Robby this."

His Father remained silent. His cheeks pulsated. He eyed his son.

Robby protectively picked up the cage and stood next to his mother.

"Isn't that nice, Charles?" his mother continued.

Robby stood stiff with fear. He knew no matter what happened he would not let go of the cage. He would hold onto it even if his Father slammed him against the wall or slapped his face until he bled. This his father could not take from him.

His Father narrowed his eyes and focused on Robby. His Mother gently touched Robby's back. Robby stood rigid.

"You put that in the cellar. That is the only place I want to see those pesty critters," his father finally said.

Robby quickly left the kitchen, carrying his cage. He stepped down the stairs to the cellar and found a place hidden in a back corner to put his cage. He carefully set it down and proudly looked at it. Now when he was cleaning the woodshop, he would have his own pets to keep him company.

CHAPTER 16

Robby's parents left him alone in the house periodically when the family went on vacations. Once alone, Robby invited the neighborhood kids over, set up his cardboard theatre stage and performed stories with his puppets for the neighborhood children. He charged them seven cents each to attend, and with the money, he bought himself a hamburger or ice cream cone at the local stores. He also spent time at the music store with Joe Rossi, who taught him how to play his guitar in exchange for polishing the instruments. Robby practiced his guitar for hours, and when he was done, he spent endless free time playing games with the neighborhood friends. He did not have to worry about food. Joe, at the music store, bought him hamburgers and paid him enough so that he could buy his own food. His mother had left him food in the refrigerator, too - potato salad, liverwurst, bread, peanut butter. Robby washed his clothes in the washer and hung them outside to dry on his mother's clothesline. At night, he sat in the living room and watched television – The Twilight Zone and the I Love Lucy show. His world was his own. He could breathe in and out freely, laugh aloud without fear, fall asleep in the living room with the television on, and walk around the house like he owned it. He could be the neighborhood friend he always wanted to be. He could freely come and go. Best of all, his teenage sister, Terry, often stayed home and let Robby hang around with her and her numerous friends. She took him to local concerts to see the musicians play.

But when his family arrived home from their weekend trips and his father's boots moved across the floor, Robby returned to the attic with the door locked so no one could get in. His confinement resumed, his downheartedness returned, and his world once again closed into a small, cold, musty, dark attic with no lighting. He was growing tall and lanky, much taller than his older brother. He had to bend low to move through the attic. He was shut off from the world. Inside the attic, he was as quiet as he could be.

A neighbor came by the house one day to talk to Robby's parents. Robby watched and listened from the open attic window to the neighbor talking to his father at the door.

"It's the weirdest thing, Charles," the neighbor said, "at night, there is someone in your attic. My wife and I can see flickers of light and movement up there. I wouldn't say anything because I figure it is someone in your family rummaging around the attic, but I wanted to mention that to my wife and me, it seems spooky, like it's a ghost or something. We see shadows moving around. It's eerie."

Robby listened. For a long moment, his father did not speak. Then he let out a weak chuckle. "Oh, that is my wife, going through old photos. She is organizing them. Funny, you should notice."

"I figured it was nothing. But my wife and I got a good laugh out of it," the neighbor said.

His Father said something that Robby did not hear, and then the door shut. From the corner of the window, Robby watched the man walk back to his house. He wondered if he would get in trouble for using a candle in the attic to see at night. It was his only source of light, and he did not want to lose it. Robby hid them under floorboards and hoped his father would not find them.

The next day, after he had scrubbed the woodshop from top to bottom, Robby snuck out the cellar door and stealthily made his way to Forbes St. He snuck into the backyard of his friend Greg's house and slipped through the broken fence that bordered the Saucony woods. The Saucony Oil Company owned the large, wooded area and had built an oil refinery on the land. But over time, they closed the refinery and completely closed off the area to the public by building a large fence around the land. Two large buildings, each with a smokestack, were now empty and locked. In front of the buildings were three large pools filled with oil. The townspeople said if you fell into one of the pools, you would drown. The large fence that surrounded the refinery kept all the people out, but the one break in the fence behind Greg's house was the perfect way to get onto the property. Several abandoned acres had grown wild and unkempt. The trees grew a tangle of branches that dipped and bent in many directions and hid the refinery from the public. Robby wandered around the silent, wild woods feeling like he had stepped into a wilderness. Tall grasses grew around the immense tree trunks. Branches stretched between the numerous trees, intertwined, and cluttered with leaves, so much so that it was hard to see which branches belonged to which trees. Only the sound of the tree leaves wrestling in the wind could be heard. Birds flew from one tree to another, watching him. Next to one refinery, he found lots of lumber lying scattered around on the ground. It was clear to Robby that no one came into this area. If he stayed away from the oil pools, he would be completely alone and safe.

He got busy. He carried the lumber to areas he thought would make good places for homemade, hidden forts. He placed the wood in the long grasses at the base of tall maple trees. He carried the lumber, one at a time, up the trees and laid them on top of intertwining branches. Once he had laid down enough for a platform that would accommodate his body, he used rope to tie the boards together. He laid large, broken branches on the platform edges to make small walls, and secured them in place with the rope, tying them to the floor so they would not fall off. Then he camouflaged his tree forts with leaves and sticks. Once they were built and he was back on the ground, he peered at his forts and marveled at the way he had hidden them so well that anyone walking below the trees would not be able to distinguish his forts from the intertwining branches. They were so close together that Robby could go from fort to fort without touching the ground. On the ground, he made numerous little hidden storage and sitting areas at the bottom of several large pine trees. These were his ground forts. For an entire weekend, he worked. Finally, he walked back to his parents' attic late Sunday evening after his family had gone to sleep. He snuck in through the cellar door. As he tiptoed past his father's workshop, he noticed that his father had been using the woodshop during the day and had left a mess, which Robby would have to clean when he arrived home from school the next afternoon. At the back of the stairs, Robby lifted himself up each step until he reached the floorboards to the attic. He pushed them inside and climbed into the attic. He placed the floorboards in their rightful spot. For the first time all weekend, he noticed the chill in the air. He wrapped himself in his thin blanket. He fell quickly asleep.

In the morning, he found a bowl of oatmeal on the floor outside the door. He ate it and got ready for school. After school, he cleaned the cellar. While he worked, he collected little items he could use in all his tree houses – old sandpaper, plumber candles, matchsticks, small pieces of discarded wood, screws, bolts, and even a small pair of old scissors. He brought all the items to the attic and waited until night fell. Then he made his way down the back of the stairs, across the cellar, and out the cellar door. In his jacket pockets were all the things he had collected. He walked through the backyards of his neighbors, searching through their garbage cans for old blankets and anything he could keep inside his forts. By the time he arrived at the Saucony woods, his pockets and hands were full, and he was clutching an old, brown blanket. He climbed one of the trees to his hidden fort. He lined the sides of his platforms with his little treasures. Then he lay on the platform and stared at the stars twinkling through the tree branches. He wondered what was out in the universe, why the stars sparkled, why the moon shone as it did every night to light his way. An owl leaped from the tallest tree branch and, with its expansive wings, gracefully flew above the treetops. Bats whizzed past him, flapping their wings, appearing to randomly fly but strategically avoiding every obstacle in their paths. His Uncle Irving had taught Robby how to see in the dark, how to focus on something dark and magically. What was next to it would suddenly reveal itself as if it were day.

"You can see everything in the dark if you learn to adjust your eyes to it," he told Robby.

The night sounds soothed, Robby. He loved to hear the wrestling leaves, the crickets chirping, the frogs croaking.

He lay listening and watching until his eyes closed. He drifted to sleep.

The next Saturday morning, his mother told him he was going to get to see the Red Sox game again with his father and brother. Robby got into the station wagon and drove off with them. Again, he was dumped on a run-down street in Boston.

"I hope I never have to see your ugly face again," his father said as he pushed Robby out of the car.

But Robby no longer felt weak and helpless. Immediately after being dumped, he made his way to the train tracks, waited for a freight train to chug around the bend and then ran beside it until it slowed enough for him to hop onto a flatbed car and travel back to Riverside, Rhode Island, where he went to Saucony woods and lazily sat in his treehouses. He had collected so many items that he stored in his hidden ground storage areas and platform houses that he could survive there on his own for the entire warm season. Jars of peanut butter, canned vegetables, cans of salmon, tuna, and a can opener. He had stolen the items from his mother's kitchen at night. He guessed she knew but allowed him the food.

Robby also stored clothes in all his platform tree houses, and when the clothes were no longer clean, he stayed overnight at his friend's houses. When he woke up in the morning, his clothes were washed and neatly folded beside him. But Robby preferred to be alone. He spent most of his time in the little homes he had built in the woods. There he was, safe. There he was free.

At school, he could not concentrate. He authored stories instead. The teachers noticed and praised him. Still, every report card that he brought home was met with a slap on the back of his head and banishment to the attic. But now he had his home outside of the dark attic. Soon after he was thrown to the attic, he escaped down the back of the stairs and out the cellar door, where he was free to live his life on his own terms.

Late one night, he roamed the neighborhood, collecting items to bring to his little hidden homes from neighbors' garbage can - a spoon, an empty tin can, an old pair of rain boots that were too large for him but would do nicely when sloshing through rainwater and mud, paper bags, an old twist topper, empty Coca-Cola bottles, a chipped salad plate. He carried these items into the Saucony woods and headed toward one of his hidden dugouts at the base of a pine tree. He reached below the branch that covered his hidden dugout only to find that someone had found his space and had stolen his possessions. The cigarette lighter and the two unsmoked Camel cigarettes inside the wrinkled pack were gone. Even though Robby did not smoke, he had coveted the ownership of two real cigarettes and had kept them. It was his one defiant move to fight against his circumstances. His old steak knife was missing. So was some paper he had found. His clothes were scattered on the ground near the hidden shelter. He gathered them into his arms and hugged them close. He sank into despair. He sat for a few minutes in the dark, staring at the black night, looking upward at the stars peeking through the tree branches. A cool wind blew through the trees. Robby was sure the wind was calling to him, carrying him beyond his defeat into the rattling embrace of the thousands of leaves. Looking upward, he knew someone out there was telling him that he only needed to look upward and ahead in life, that somehow, he would endure, surrounded by the natural rhythm of the tree leaves singing to him, or the owl swooping by him, or the bats flying as close as they could before they abruptly turned away. When he felt better, he took all his belongings and put them in a paper bag, then quickly, like a coyote in the night, carried them to his giant maple tree, climbed it all the way up to his platform house, and hid his remaining belongings underneath a pile of leaves. Then he lay there and let his mind wander. An idea came to him. He could collect old paint cans and stash them in the fields, so people walking by would think they were just rusty old, discarded cans scattered around. No one would bother to look inside them, but inside them, he could hide his food and clothes and other little treasures he found.

The next day, he collected old tin cans from neighbors' garbage cans. He strategically placed them in open areas, some behind his parents' house at the bottom of large trees just beyond their property, some just beyond the fence that encircled the local cemetery, some at the Mill ponds near Barrington, and some in Saucony woods. He never put much into each of them, just some non-perishable food that could withstand the fluctuating weather elements. He memorized where he put everything in the tall, wild grasses and frequently checked on them as often as he could.

Willow trees were Robby's favorite tree. In Riverside, willow trees were everywhere, even in Saucony Oil woods. The branches were strong and elastic. At the base of one that grew next to his platform forts, Robby pulled a branch down, wrapped his hands around it, yanked it, and then let go. He sprung upward and landed with ease with his feet firmly planted on his treehouse platform. When he wanted down, he grabbed a branch and rode it down to the ground. Using his knife and string, he cut some branches to make his first bow and arrow. He banged a rock against a smaller rock over and over until he had chiseled the rock into an arrow tip. He tied it to the end of a small branch, and his arrow was complete. The first time he used it, he shot a crow and killed it. When he saw what he had done, he was so overcome with grief for killing one of nature's creatures that he cried. To help himself through his grief, he buried the bird and made a cross out of sticks to mark the grave. Then he broke up his bow and arrow and lit it on fire with his lighter and watched it burn.

At home, it was clear that something was wrong with his mother. She spent most of her time in bed, languishing in complete exhaustion and fatigue. She had two more young girls and struggled to get through her daily chores. She often cried and went every week to the doctor.

Robby often visited her while she lay in her bed. "What's wrong, Mom?"

His mother pulled him to her bedside. "I am sorry, Robby. I cannot help this."

Robby stood with his hands in his pockets.

"I am a victim of unrequited love, Robby. This is something you cannot yet understand, I know." She patted his hand. "No matter what your father tells me to do, I must do it. My whole life, I have tried to love, and it has never been reciprocated." Beside her bed were several harlequin romance novels piled on a nightstand.

Robby was confused. He did not understand what his mother meant. He did not know how to respond.

"Do you know what it means to be paranoid?" she asked him.

Paranoid was a word he had never heard before. He shook his head. His mother's words were frightening him. "I'm paranoid," she whispered. Her face told him she was completely defeated.

She rolled over and covered her face with her hand. The only person in the world who genuinely loved him was hurt and sick. He wondered if he was like his mom. He often lay in his bed full of despair a nd sadness, wondering what he had done wrong in life. Did his mother feel the same way?

Robby sat next to her while she lay in bed, listless and defeated. Yet, his concern did not seem to make her better. One day, she got up and returned to her motherly duties in the household. Nothing more was ever discussed. But Robby knew she was not completely well. She still made frequent visits to the doctor and had completely stopped smiling.

Robby needed love and affection. He often wandered around the neighborhood by himself. He longed to have a family. Standing in empty fields, he looked at his house and wished he could visit his sisters and his mother, but his father's truck was in the driveway. Self-preservation had settled inside him. The enemy lived inside the house. So, he played with the neighborhood boys. They often walked past the Saucony Oil woods to old man Leonardo's farm and trespassed on his farm to climb his trees. One day, they rested on the branches and watched the cows graze his grasslands. Matthew thought it would be fun to jump from the branch onto the back of a cow and ride it across the field. When a cow lingered below him, he leapt off his branch onto its back and landed with his legs spread on either side of it,

firmly on its back. The cow ran and bucked her hind legs.
Matthew catapulted off the cow and pounded onto the
ground. Robby and his friends laughed. Matthew stood and
dusted the dirt off his pants. They all decided to try it. One
by one, they leapt off their branch onto a cow's back and
tried to ride the cow as if they were bronc-riding a bull. Each
time they fell off. The farmer drove up, got his shotgun out
of his truck, and began shooting it in the direction of the
boys. The boys all quickly scrambled down the trees and ran
as fast as they could off Leonardo's land.

Robby would have stayed off the farm for good, but
he loved that farm. It was the only place he could go that
reminded him of his Uncle Irving and Aunt May's farm. He
knew the day farmer Leonardo had shot at him and his
friends for jumping on his cows. He had fired his shotgun
upward and away from them. The old farmer was only trying
to scare them off. Robby was not deterred from going onto
his property. He loved to visit the stream there, so he
returned over and over to watch the crawdads, catch the
turtles and fish, and climb the trees that stretched over the
stream. He often scooped the crawdads up in his hands and
cracked their shells. He ate the delicious meat raw. The extra
meat did not fill his empty belly, but any food helped.

One day, Robby was stretched out on his stomach at
the edge of the stream catching crawdads when the farmer
approached him from behind.

"You like the stream, don't you?" the farmer asked
him in a quiet voice.

Startled, Robby leapt to his hands and knees and then
quickly stood. He thought he was in trouble now. If his

father found out he was trespassing on Leonardo's farm, he would endure another hard slap.

"Yes, sir," Robby said, sounding confident, but his mind raced with worry. Would the farmer tell his dad that he was trespassing on farmland?

"I did not intend to harm you or your friends a while back. I wanted to scare you all off."

"I know," Robby said. "I apologize for my behavior."

"You must understand that you could have severely harmed my cows. I depend on them to provide me with milk. That is how I make my living. You understand?"

"I do," Robby replied.

"I'll tell you what," the farmer said. "If you keep your friends off my property, I'll let you fish in my stream all you want."

Robby looked at him and nodded. "I will," he answered, relieved to be allowed another food source.

Old man, Leonardo sized Robby up and down. Robby pulled at his shirt to make it look like it fit him appropriately, then released it only to have it bounce upward, revealing his lean abdomen. He shuffled his feet, hoping the farmer overlooked his toe sticking out of his torn sneakers and the loose rubber sole hanging to its side. But the farmer was not dressed much neater than Robby. He wore bibbed denim overalls. One strap hung loosely down his side. His weathered face was littered with stubs of hair.

The farmer looked at Robby and said, "You will?"

"I promise I will," Robby said. "I won't let them on your property."

"Good," the farmer said, "Then it is a deal. You keep your friends away from my cows, and you can fish in my stream."

Robby wanted to smile, but smiling could get him in trouble. He knew better than to reveal any pleasure. "It's a deal."

Old man Leonardo, a milk and beef farmer, turned and walked away, leaving Robby to continue his quest to catch all the crawdads he could find to eat.

Robby kept his word and kept his friends off the farmer's property. He told his friends that old man Leonardo would get them the next time they trespassed on his land. But Robby need not have bothered scaring his friends off Leonardo's land. After they had been shot at, none of them wanted to venture onto his land anymore.

CHAPTER 17

Robby's conversations with his father and mother were minimal. Increasingly, he was on his own, living in Saucony Woods and hunting and fishing for food. He kept stashes of his clothes in several locations. In a thriving town of working-class families, only Robby was fending for himself in the woods to survive. The rest of the towns' people lived in warm houses and ate an abundance of food, celebrated holidays with extended family, and slept in warm beds. No one knew Robby's dire plight, and he was determined to keep it hidden from everyone. The best way for him to survive was to pretend that he was fine.

Robby's father bought a huge swath of land in Maine near the water. He planned to build a new community of homes. The family made the decision to move full-time to Maine to build the homes. Whatever had gone wrong with his mom, she seemed better. She had forgiven his father, and they were moving to Maine to make a fresh start. The entire family was going. His two older sisters and his older brother packed their clothes. His mother packed her clothes, her husband's and Robby's two younger sisters' clothes. They packed up the house and temporarily closed it for the move. Eventually, his mother said, after they had built the vacation homes, they planned to move back to Riverside, Rhode Island and return home.

Robby sat on his chair in the attic listening to their bustling movements below in the house. No one had said it. No one had told him. But he knew he was not going with them. The realization sat like a jagged knife inside his stomach, slicing him every time he heard his sister's laughter, every time he heard a suitcase shut and then dragged outside to the car for the trip north.

Someone knocked on his door. "Robby," his mother called. "Open the door. I have something important to tell you."

Robby sat up. He stood. As he walked to unlock his door, he wondered what his mother would say to him. Was she going to tell him he was not going? Or was she coming to tell him to hurry and pack? But even as Robby approached the door, he knew from the sound of his mother's voice that something was terribly wrong with her. Instead of her usual forced cheerfulness, her voice sounded urgent and impatient.

He opened it.

His mother took his hand. She frowned, her eyes wet and bloodshot, her nose red. She looked older than she did a week ago. "Come with me."

Robby stepped down the stairs behind her and followed her into her bedroom. He rarely went into the room where his parents slept, but he knew his mother kept the bed made and the room free from clutter. Two open suitcases sat on the bed, and his parents' clothes were neatly packed inside them.

His mother went to her dresser, leaned down, and opened the bottom drawer. Robby leaned over and looked down to see several shirts and sweaters neatly folded inside. She pushed the items aside and reached into the back, and pulled out a small box. She opened it. The box had an envelope in it. "This will be our secret space. No one else needs to know. We can exchange information here. Put anything you need to give me in here, and I will put the information I need to tell you in here too. She opened the envelope and pulled out a key. "Put this in your pocket. This is a key to the house, so you can get inside."

Robby turned his eyes from the key to her face. The world stopped. He believed he had finally been completely erased from his family.

His mother grabbed him and hugged him to her chest, breathing in deeply and then sighing. "I have to say goodbye to you. I am sorry. I have not done my duty with you."

Robby choked back his emotions. He had many words he would like to say, but if he opened his mouth, a cry might escape, and he could not have that now. Instead, he released his mom and took the key from her. He put it in his pocket.

She leaned down, closed the box, placed it in the drawer, and shut the drawer. "Remember, you can leave me things in here, and I will leave you things too." She stood and looked at him. The color had drained from her face. The skin under her eyes was puffy.

Robby turned and walked out of the bedroom and into the kitchen. His siblings ran to the car to get inside it. His mother came into the kitchen carrying both big suitcases. She wobbled a bit. Robby took one of her suitcases and carried it out of the kitchen door to the car. His father sat in the driver's seat, his hands gripping the steering wheel, looking impatient and angry. His baby sisters, Alice and the new baby, Paula, were in the back seat. Terry sat beside them. Nancy and Darin were in the back seats, sitting near the suitcases, all in a row. Robby put the suitcase next to them, then ran back to his mother and took her other one. He carried it to the back and loaded it into the rear of the car, and then closed the door. He walked to the passenger side and helped his mother into her seat, and shut the door.

His mother faced ahead. His father started the engine. Robby felt his heart drop. He stepped away and stood with his hands at his side. He glanced at his father. His face was distorted into a wild, angry grimace.

He looked at his mother. She rested her head on her seat and looked at him. She looked horrified. He saw how sad she was at having to abandon him. He felt so sorry for her. She was like a little wounded bird that had lost her wings.

His father looked at Robby and sucked in his breath as if gathering up all his anger for one loud outburst. Then he yelled, "Get the hell away from my car!"

Robby's breath caught in his throat. He refused to cry. The car carrying his family backed down the driveway, exhaust-spewing out in a cloud around him. He breathed it in, all the toxic fumes, the endless grit and grime of his life, the slaps, the rejection, the realization that he was no longer wanted, had never been wanted. Bent over like a broken twig, he watched his family's station wagon careen down the road. Robby caught the stricken look on his mother's face. In it, he saw her fear. Her eyes reached him, begging him to survive.

As they drove away, Robby watched them, wondering what they were thinking, if they would miss him, if they would think of him from time to time, if they even cared if he survived. He wondered if his mother was crying if she had begged his father to turn back, pick him up, and take him with them. Surely, they just cannot drive away and completely leave him. He was just a scrawny twelve-year-old. He was just a thin boy with stick legs that hurt sometimes to walk on. Didn't they care? No, it cannot be. They would return for him, just drive around the block, return, and take him in their car with them. It was just one of his father's sick jokes. But as he stood, he understood. They were never coming. They would never return. He was completely on his own. Robby turned away.

But, as Robby walked toward the house, he began to feel stronger. He was ok. He was better than ok. He was, for the first time in his life, completely free from his oppressor, finally liberated from being smacked and forced to live in isolation. A sense of power and complete self-control raced through his body. Gone was the frightened little boy who had been confused and scared each time he had been dropped off and left wandering the Boston streets, fearful of strangers, lost and alone. Now he could finally live on his own terms.

Confidently, he walked toward the house, his hand in his pocket, his fingers feeling the key. The brilliant sun warmed him. The wind caressed him, comforted him, blowing him toward a life he could live on his own terms. When he walked into the house, he had the feeling like no one could stop him now. Never again would he be slapped. Never again would he be isolated. He had been suddenly uncaged and liberated.

He walked through his father's workshop, feeling like he now owned all the table saws and the wood. He climbed the stairs into the kitchen. He poured himself a large glass of water and gulped it down. He could live here free and clear from harm for a long time. He was free to go from room to room. He sank into his father's coveted chair and put his legs over the armchair, and freely dangled them. He watched the television for a while. Then he went into all three bedrooms and decided he would sleep on his brother's bed. His only problem would be finding food. He would no longer have the family meal scraps left at the attic doorway to survive on. He did not have any money. The thought of sustaining himself only on the fish he caught did not appeal to him. He searched the kitchen and found no food in the house. His mother had cleaned it all out.

Robby waited until the next night before he left the house. He needed food, and he needed a lot of it. But where? The town had fallen into its nighttime slumber. He rummaged through the neighbor's garbage but did not find anything he could eat. He passed through the backyards of his neighbors' homes and then crossed the street into the cemetery. The tombstones loomed large against the full moon. Tree branches dangled above him. He zigzagged through the graveyard and hopped the fence. He followed the path to the waterfront, where a row of restaurants ran along a road. In the alleyway behind the restaurants, he dug through the garbage cans for scraps of food. He found a large amount of pasta mixed with spaghetti sauce. Ravenously, he scooped it into his mouth with his hands. His stomach full, he made his way to the Saucony woods and climbed into one of the tree houses. He fell into a deep, peaceful sleep among the only thing in the world that genuinely loved him – nature.

Late every night, he dug through the garbage bins behind an Italian restaurant. Finding just enough edible spaghetti, he was able to sustain himself. But he wanted a real meal, one that was not all jumbled into a bunch of scraps. His growing body needed nourishment. He became bolder. At the end of each night, he sat by the garbage bin to wait for the man to come out of the restaurant with the nightly garbage scraps. He wanted to ask him for food but didn't.

Finally, after a week, the man said to him. "What are you doing out here, son? You ok? You hungry?"

Robby froze.

"Where's your family?"

Robby put his head down and shook it.

"You want something to eat?" The man said.

Robby nodded.

"Come inside. I will get you something to eat."

Robby followed him inside the restaurant. The dim-lighted dining area was empty, except for two men who were wiping tables and stacking the chairs. Robby smelled the Italian aromas of basil and garlic. He imagined the food sliding down his throat and into his empty belly. He shifted his legs back and forth impatiently, waiting. The empty pit of his stomach reminded him how desperate he was for food.

The man told Robby to sit at the table. He sat down.

"You got family in town, kid?" the man asked Robby.

Robby did not respond. The last thing he wanted anyone to know was that he was alone.

"Do ya?" the man repeated.

Robby slightly shook his head.

"What you want, kid?" the man asked. "You can have anything, spaghetti, lasagna, ravioli."

Robby looked up at him. He placed his hands on the table and folded them. "I'd like a hot plate of spaghetti and meatballs with parmesan cheese sprinkled on top, garlic bread, a salad, and a glass of red wine."

The man chuckled. He placed his hands on his hips. "A glass of red wine?"

"Yes. Your best one." Robby folded the napkin on his lap and looked up at the man.

He shook his head and smiled. "Coming up, kid. You got it."

When the food arrived, Robby attempted to eat it using good manners, but his hunger overcame any desire he had to make a good impression. He gobbled it down, then drank the wine with gusto. He wiped his mouth with the back of his hand.

The man approached Robby again. "Kid, you got a place to sleep?"

Robby did not answer.

"You go to school?"

"Yes," Robby said.

"What grade you in?" the man asked.

"Seventh grade."

"Where are your parents?"

Robby leaned back in his chair. "They're gone."

"You on your own?"

"I get by," Robby answered.

"I see that, by the way, you're starving." The man crossed his arms and looked at Robby.

He was tall and big around his waist. But Robby was not afraid. Any man who would feed him a meal fit for royalty was not an enemy.

"What's your name?"

Robby looked at the man. He was about to say his nickname – Robby – but changed his mind. Robby was a kid's name. He was not a kid. In truth, he had not been a kid for a long time. He straightened and looked at the man. "Bob," he said. "I'm Bob." From now on, he would only respond to being called Bob. Robby had been a victim. Bob would not be.

"I tell you what, Bob," the man said. "You go ahead and sleep tonight in one of my booths and then come by tomorrow after school, and I'll give you a job washing dishes."

"Thank you." A tremendous weight lifted off Bob's shoulders. He knew how to work hard, and he would regularly be fed a satisfying meal. The pit in his stomach suddenly disappeared. He had achieved his first independent victory.

"I'm Giovanni, the owner. You will be my dishwasher. Be back here by 5 p.m. tomorrow. I will play you two dollars an hour, cash." He turned to leave. "And kid," he turned back, "come cleaned up."

Bob was pleased. Two dollars an hour was more than minimum wage. "Thank you."

Bob slept well, curled on the black leather seat that wound around the table. The temperature was comfortably warm, not like the house where the heater had been turned off. The next morning before the sun came up, when the cook arrived, he slipped out the back door and ran home. He entered the house through the back door and went into the bathroom. He got into the bathtub and scrubbed his body with some detergent he found under the kitchen sink, and washed his hair. When he was done, he smelled like a spring garden. He put on clean clothes. Then he quickly snuck out of the house before the neighborhood awakened and ran to Saucony Woods to await the time he would need to go to school. He climbed a tree to one of his tree houses and waited for the moment the sun rose enough in the sky for school to start. As he waited, he reveled in the knowledge that he had found a way to solve his hunger problem. In fact, he was solving all his problems. Best of all, he was free from his father's wrath. But he would miss his mother terribly. He would miss sitting at the kitchen table while she cooked the family meals. He would miss hearing his mother sing. Her voice was pure, and strong and rose up in the house like a sweet breeze that chased his father's toxic air away. How she loved to make pies, humming as she stretched the pie dough over the pie pan and then poured in the apple mixture of apple slices, cinnamon, butter, and sugar. She covered it with pie crust and squeezed the sides together. Then, as a treat for Bob, she made him his own small pie to take into the attic with him. Those secret moments gave Bob the courage to carry on. Now she was gone, for good.

When the sun came up, Bob climbed down the tree and hurried to school. He arrived early and waited for the door to open, and then ran to his classroom. Halfway through the school day, his stomach rumbled. He became fidgety and unable to concentrate on his lessons. It was hard to concentrate on an empty stomach, but he managed to finish the work.

During the lunch hour, Bob did not bother sitting with the other children to watch them eat their lunch. He did not have money to purchase lunch from the school cafeteria, nor had he brought his own lunch. Watching his classmates happily eating was more than he could bear. Instead, he found a corner under the stairwell and waited for the lunch hour to end.

After school, Bob ran to the restaurant. He burst into it and stood at the entrance, suddenly not knowing what to do. He watched the waiters and cooks bustling around, getting ready to open the restaurant for the evening. Finally, Giovanni walked into the dining room and saw Bob standing at the entrance.

Giovanni threw up in his hands in a friendly gesture. "You made it, kid!"

Bob smiled. Over time, he had gotten skilled at hiding his hunger, but his hands fidgeted a bit. His lean body gave away his obvious lack of nourishment. Still, he worked to hide it.

Giovanni motioned him inside. "Let's get you something to eat. Then you can get to work."

Bob followed him.

"You made it to school, kid?" Giovanni motioned him to sit down at a table.

"Yes, I did my classwork," Bob said, sitting down.

"Good, good. That's what I like to hear." Giovanni left the room for a bit and returned with a large spaghetti dinner, complete with French bread and butter.

Bob tried his best to be polite. "Thank you." He did not waste any time picking up the fork and diving into the dinner. He rolled the spaghetti onto his fork and slopped it into his mouth, then furiously ate more.

Giovanni watched him, his hand at his chin, his eyebrows pinched, his eyes steadily watching Bob shove food into his mouth. He scratched his chin, but Bob did not give Giovanni more than a second glance. He was so happy to be given a decent meal that at that moment, the entire world surrounding him had completely disappeared except for his spaghetti dinner.

"You know, son," Giovanni said, "if you are going to work for me, you must attend school every day. You also must stay clean and sober. No drugs, no stealing, no cheating in school. You understand?"

Bob nodded. "I understand."

"No going down the wrong path in life? You understand?"

"Yes," Bob said, digesting all Giovanni said. "I promise."

"Good. That's what I like to hear. You work for me, I take care of you, but you got to live by my rules, and that means no getting into trouble," he said.

"You have my word," Bob said, and he meant to keep it.

"I do not tolerate any unruly behavior. You go to school and then come work for me," Giovanni repeated.

"I will," Bob said. "Thank you."

When Bob was done eating, Giovanni took him into the dishwashing area. "You stand here and wait for the dirty dishes to be brought to you by the bus-boy." He taught Bob how to clean the dishes and place them on the rack to drip-dry.

When he left, Bob got busy. Like a dishwashing pro, he threw a hand towel over his shoulder and dove into his job. He washed each dish until it was completely clean and then stacked it on the drying racks. When they were dry, he placed them on the kitchen counter for the cooks to reuse. The room was warm but fans blowing above him cooled him down. He knew how important it was to complete his job thoroughly without any smudges or specks of food left on the dishes. Some of the big, heavy pots were hard to wash but he thrust his entire body into his job, standing on his tiptoes, if necessary, to reach the entire workload. He would not let Giovanni down.

Every night Bob washed the dishes for nine hours straight, working hard, grateful for the work and food. After the store closed, ten or twelve of Giovanni's Italian friends gathered at the restaurant to play cards until late in the night. The chubby, cigar-smoking men ran small gambling bets. Bob hung around and served the men their drinks, brought them their food, cleaned their ashtrays, and did whatever else they asked for.

"Hey, Giovanni," one man said, a cigar dangling from his mouth, "what's up with the kid?"

"That's Bobby," Giovanni said.

"How come he's here?" one asked.

"He just showed up one day. He won't leave," Giovanni said, then winked at Bob.

"Hey Bobby!" one of them said to him.

'He works for me. Leave the kid alone," Giovanni said.

'He's young," one of the men said, then took a puff on his fat cigar.

Giovanni waved his hand. "Nothing happens to this kid."

Then one called Bob over to him. "Hey, Bobby, come here. Tell me something about yourself."

What are ya doing?" Giovanni said, "Leave him alone. Don't be messing with the kid. He's a good kid. He's working for me now."

One guy got up and went to Bob. He stuck fifty dollars in his pocket. "Run down the street to the corner restaurant, Vinnies, and tell Vinnie that John says he's an ass hole. Then come right back to me."

Bob did as he was asked. He walked down the street, knocked on the restaurant door, and a man answered. "What's up, Kid?"

"You Vinnie?" Bob said.

"Yeah." Vinnie said.

"John says you're an ass hole."

"He did?" Vinnie said. "You go back to John and tell him I say he's a fucking ass hole."

Bob ran back to Giovanni's and walked over to the men.

"Hey, kid," John said. "Did you do what I said?"

"Yeah."

"What did he say?"

"He said to tell you that you're a fucking ass hole."

All the guys laughed. Then another guy said, "Bobby, come over here." He waved Bob toward him.

Bob went to him, and he stuck a hundred-dollar bill in Bob's pocket. "Go to Vinnie's restaurant, give him these papers, and tell them he needs to tip you. Tell him Alonzo sent you. Then, come right back here." Alonzo gave Bob the envelope and leaned back in his chair and puffed a cigar.

Bob ran down the nighttime street, knocked on Vinnie's door, and gave the envelope to him. "It's from Alonzo. He says you have to tip me."

Vinnie peeked inside the envelope and then closed it. He waved for Bob to follow him. Vinnie went into a back room and sat down at his desk. He leaned back in his chair. The smell of cigarettes lingered in the air. "He said I had to tip you, did he?" He reached into his pocket and pulled out fifty dollars, and gave it to Bob.

Bob pocketed the money, turned, and ran back to the restaurant. He burst into the dining area. The men were busy playing cards. In the dim lighting, the cigar smoke hovered above the men. The ice in the glasses clinked. The chairs creaked under the weight of the men as they shifted around.

"Hey, Bobby! You do as I say?" Alonzo took a sip of his drink and swirled the ice in the glass.

"Yes," Bob said.

"How much he tip ya?"

"Fifty."

"Fifty! The man's a cheapskate. You run back over there and tell Vinnie I say he's a cheapskate," Alonzo said.

Bob left the restaurant, ran back to Vinnies and burst into his office. Vinnie was busy counting a large stash of money. "Alonzo says to tell you you're a cheapskate."

Vinnie stopped counting and looked at Bob. "Did he now?" He reached into his pocket and handed Robby a one-hundred-dollar bill. "You go back to Alonzo and tell him I say he's an ass hole."

Bob ran back to the restaurant and burst inside. He went straight to Alonzo. "Vinnie says you're an ass hole."

All the men laughed. "Did he give you more money?" Alonzo asked Bob.

"Yeah, he gave me $100.00."

The men all laughed. "That'll teach him," Alonzo said.

From then on, Bob became their daytime and nighttime errand boy, running the winnings to other restaurants. He never looked inside the envelope. The men trusted Bob and he wanted their trust. He proved himself to be reliable. In exchange for the added money, he promised to attend school, not smoke cigarettes, nor do drugs. He promised to be a model student and he carried through with the promises. He could not believe he was given money for doing nothing. He had never even seen a one-hundred-dollar bill before. But now, over just a brief period, he had hundreds of dollars. He stashed them in the attic, under a floorboard in a small box. Never again would he be hungry. And, best of all, he was safe.

For the first time he was free of injuries. He was no longer shoved into the walls or backhanded across the face. The scar on his cheek from his father's pencil stabbing him looked like a dimple but, of course, was not. People told him, "What a sweet dimple you have," and Bob did not correct them. Despite the obvious scars, Bob was gaining health. He was gaining much-needed weight and shooting up in height. He had plenty of money to buy food and other necessary supplies. He walked to the stores and bought new clothes. He even bought some black leather shoes, the first new shoes he had ever owned.

For the first time, Bob felt safe too. Around Giovanni's friends, while they played cards at the end of each night, Bob felt he belonged. He did everything he could to make their nightly visits comfortable. He emptied their ashtrays, lifted their dirty plates off the table and washed them, filled their scotch and ice-water drinks, and whatever else they needed. He was quickly becoming the restaurant owners' beloved son, as loved as their own biological sons. No one ever spoke about his abandonment, and it was clear they had taken Bob as one of their own. For the first time in his life, Bob was healthy.

Giovanni made a point of protecting him and voicing it to his friends. "Don't let nothing bad happen to our Bobby. He's a good kid. I don't want nothing bad to ever happen to him."

The men nodded and continued their card game, their laughter, their heavy drinking in the dim-lighted closed restaurant. No one in Riverside Rhode Island knew about these secret card games. They discussed their bets, their winnings, and although Bob could not hear a lot of what was discussed in their low whispers, he knew they were up to important work.

After a while, the men called Bob over. Alonzo wrapped his arm around his waist. "How you doing, son? You getting along? You staying clean? Going to school?"

Bob nodded. "I am."

"Good, son. The kids treating you well in school."

"There is a group of kids that hang out at the street corner here. They tease me, chase me, and try to hit me. I have to run away," Bob said.

Alonzo rubbed the stubbles on his chin. "They do, do they? Well, don't you worry about them no more?"

The next day when Bob passed the mean boys on the way to the restaurant, the boys put their heads down and walked away. Bob was stunned. He expected to be beaten by the kids one day, but now they were running away from him.

As the days and weeks passed, he realized that every time he complained to the restaurant owners about being harassed by other kids, the harassment suddenly ceased. All he had to do was turn to the men and everyone in the town stopped bothering him.

Every day, Giovanni asked Bob, "Did you go to school?"

'Yes," Bob said.

"Did you pass?"

"Yes," Bob said.

"The teachers treating you ok?" Mr. Giovanni looked at Bob, concerned.

"They are," Bob said.

Giovanni's face relaxed. "Good, good. That's what I like to hear."

Bob would not let his boss down. He got busy washing the dishes.

After a few months, he walked to his parents' house after school to find his father's car in the driveway. Quickly, he hid in the brush. He could not go inside the house. Instead of showering and getting ready for work, he left and went to the restaurant to work his shift. When he was done for the night, he went back to his house to see if he could figure out why his father's car was parked in the driveway. In the dark, he peeked into the windows, but it was late, and the house was quiet and dark. His immediate concern was that he needed some of the money he had hidden in the attic. He opened the cellar door, climbed into the basement, and closed the door. Then he snuck across the clean woodshop and climbed up the back of the staircase into the attic. Once inside, he quietly lifted the floorboards and pulled out a box that he used to store his cash. In only a few months since his parents had deserted him, he had saved a considerable amount of money. He opened the box and

pulled out enough money to last him for a while, then hid
the money back under the floorboard. He stuffed the money
into his jacket pocket and then made his way back down the
back of the stairwell and through the woodshop to the cellar
door. He opened the cellar door and entered the cool night.
He closed the door and hurried behind the houses to
Saucony Woods. When he entered the woods and walked
among the numerous trees that surrounded him, he felt a
lightness in his steps. He shuffled through the leaves scattered
on the ground, looking at the abundance of tree branches
that stretched above him under the moonlight. He basked in
the safety the land offered him. By the time he climbed his
favorite tall tree, stepped onto the platform home, and settled
his lanky body along his strong platform, he was relaxed and
comfortable. He never belonged in his father's home, but
here he would always belong. He lay, embraced under the
canopy of branches and the silence of the still night. For the
first time, he felt at peace with the world around him. For
now, he was content. His belly full, he slept well in the cool
breeze that soothed him, the full moon shining just for him,
letting him know that something better in this world would
come his way.

A few days later, his father's car was gone. He guessed
his family had come home for the weekend and had gone
back to Maine to continue their work. Never again would he
think his father would not come back. The house was his
father's and always would be. Bob knew he did not belong
there. But he could stay in the house while his family was
gone or, if necessary, go into the attic. He could be like a
stealthy black bat in the night, moving silently through the

house while his evil father slept. He had not won his battle with his father, but he had put some distance between them.

CHAPTER 18

At school, Bob hid his abandonment. In the morning, he always arrived early and waited for the door to open and then ran to his classroom. He maintained the false pretense that he lived with his parents. When a parental signature was needed, he forged his father's name. He told his teacher that his father came home on weekends from his job in Maine to take care of family issues. He apologized politely for his father's absence, and the school accepted his excuses. When his parents missed their parent-teacher conferences, Bob covered for them, saying they would contact the school soon. To maintain his freedom, Bob became a more dutiful student, quiet and indiscreet, preferring to appear lost in the mass of students by his perfect behavior.

Bob thought he had the teachers and the entire school fooled, but one day he was sent to the school's disciplinarian's office. As Bob walked to his office, he wondered what he had done to be called in to see him. He thought he had done an excellent job of hiding his circumstances. Bob reached his office and knocked on the closed door. He stood rigid, waiting to be called in.

Mr. Ryan opened the door. "Yes, Robert Begin. Come in and take a seat." He stepped aside and let Bob inside.

Bob entered his office, trying to appear nonchalant but inside, his nerves were getting the best of him. On the wall was a photo of Mr. Ryan with a family. Bob sat down and stuck his hands inside his clenched thighs. Mr. Ryan sat down on his swivel chair. An older man with thin hair, he had a few extra pounds on him. Bob noticed his report card sitting on the desk and knew something unpleasant was about to be discussed with him.

Mr. Ryan picked up Bob's report card. "I noticed you are changing your grades on your report card and forging your father's signature. Can you tell me why?"

Bob did not know what to say. His deception had been caught. For a long time now, he had thought about quitting school. If he were now told to have his father legitimately sign his report cards, he would have to quit. He remained silent.

Mr. Ryan said, "The rule is that parents must sign their children's report card. It is important for your parents to know how you are doing in school."

Bob could not bring his report cards home to his father. "I'll have to quit school if I have to show my grades to my dad."

Mr. Ryan pinched his eyebrows and looked intently at Bob for a moment. "What's going on at home?"

"I can't bring my report card home to my father," Bob said.

Mr. Ryan looked perplexed. "Why?"

Bob let out a deep sigh. "My father will punish me. He will backhand me across my face and send me to the attic for six weeks without food. And he is not home now. He is in Maine."

"I see." Mr. Ryan rubbed his chin. He looked like he was thinking about something. "How long has this been going on?"

"All my life," Bob said.

Mr. Ryan nodded. He paused for a moment. He glanced at the family photo on the wall. He looked back at

Bob. His eyes moved from Bob's face and slowly down his body, all the way from his shoulders down to his shoes.

Bob braced himself for more discipline, more problems, but he had an out. He could quit. He looked at Mr. Ryan's face to see if he could guess what he was thinking by his expression. All his life, he had used his ability to read faces to help him know what to expect, but Mr. Ryan was not easy to read.

Mr. Ryan leaned forward. "I have a plan for you. From now on, at the grading period, instead of bringing your report card home to your parents, bring it in to me. We will go over it and work out any issues and discuss ways to improve."

Bob leaned back in his chair. He was not expecting that response.

"I will sign your report card, so your father does not have to sign it anymore. Is that a deal?"

"Yes." Bob relaxed.

"But I want you here at school every day," Mr. Ryan said. "No dropping out."

"Okay," Bob said. "Am I excused now?"

"Yes. Go back to class." Mr. Ryan stood.

Bob stood. He walked to the door. As he was exiting, he turned back to Mr. Ryan and nodded. "Thank you."

From then on, the school changed for Bob. Instead of sending notes home, Bob's teachers went to Mr. Ryan for support. The teachers modified Bob's assignments, sent Mr. Ryan notes when Bob was struggling in class. Mr. Ryan brought Bob to his office often to go over his grades and talk to him about any school issues. By the semester's end, everyone knew Bob was under Mr. Ryan's care. His parents were no longer contacted.

At the edge of east Riverside, old man Ed Daft owned a car mechanic shop. Bob often walked by the brick shop, peeking into it to watch old man Ed work on the numerous cars. Old man Ed knew Bob was continuously snooping around. Behind the shop was a muddy field filled with junky, old cars. Curious about the cars, Bob regularly went behind the shop, trudged through the mud, and peeked inside the cars, lifting the hoods to look at parts that made the cars run. He studied the parts under the hood to figure out how the parts fit together. As soon as old man Ed spied Bob perusing his old cars, he ran out the door and chased Bob off.

Old man Ed's son, Eddy, saw his dad chase Bob off one time and said, "I know that kid. He is the little brother of my friend, Terry. We often took him along when we went places. He is a good kid."

Old man Ed called to Bob. "Hey, you kid, come over here and introduce yourself."

Bob dropped his dirty hands to his side and warily stepped along the wet ground until he reached the back of the shop. He looked at old man Ed. Everyone in town knew him. He was the best mechanic. Everyone brought their cars to him. Bob respected the man and wanted to make a good impression.

Old man Ed wiped his soiled hands on his dirty towel and looked intently at Bob. "What's your name?"

"Bob, sir."

"What's your interests here?"

"I like your old cars," Bob said, being brief, then added, "I want to learn how to fix them."

"That so," Old man Ed paused. "I'll tell you what. Come into the shop and watch me fix the brakes on that car." He pointed to the blue Chevy in the shop, the hood open, the car sitting over a pit.

Bob followed him into the old, brick building and perused the shop. Hundreds of tools were placed on shelves along the walls. The sharp smell of oil and motor residue comingled in the cool air. Three cars were in the garage. Two had their hoods open with towels resting on top of the bumpers. The chevy was parked over a pit. Bob sat on a wooden box and watched old man Ed replace the car's back brakes and then the front brakes. Old man Ed explained to Bob everything he was doing. Bob watched Ed work. After a while, Ed asked Bob to hand him some tools. Bob got the tools he asked for and brought them to him. Bob brought him clean towels, oil cans, buckets, trays, and whatever old man Ed needed. If there was anything important his father had taught him, it was to be respectful, quiet, and polite, which Bob could do with ease. Watching Ed work on the cars was educational for Bob. Just to see that you could put parts together to make a working machine that moved down the street thrilled him. To Bob, the car was beginning to feel like one big giant button box full of working parts that all fit together.

Then, to Bob's surprise, Ed took the new brakes off and said to Bob, "Now you do it."

After initial hesitancy, Bob took the brakes from Ed and lay under the car. He remained silent as he took the tools, one at a time that Ed had used, and fastened the brakes onto the car. He worked much slower, not wanting to make a mistake. Mostly, he wanted his teacher to know that he could do the work. This was the first time a grown man beside Joe Rossi at the music shop had taken an interest in teaching him something. He wanted to make sure he did not let the expert mechanic down. When Bob screwed on the last bolt and pulled out from under the car, he looked at his teacher and slightly smiled. The older man could not know how much it meant to Bob that he took an interest in him.

Ed slightly tapped Bob's back, signaling his approval. "Good job, young man. I'll tell you what. You come by every day, and I will let you work here."

"Thank you," Bob whispered. He would not let him down.

After a long training that involved understanding how cars ran, the tools used to fix them, and how to get under the car in the pit to do the work, Bob started doing brake jobs for Ed every Saturday. He did four brake jobs a day and was paid $2.00 an hour. Every moment Bob was not in school or working at the restaurant, he was at old man Ed's garage helping him. Ed embraced Bob's enthusiasm for cars and began teaching him how to fix all the broken parts of the cars. He showed him how to spot what was wrong with a car by listening to its engine rumble or by listening to the sound the car made when you turned the ignition key. He taught him how to diagnose car problems that were not obvious.

Running the shop alone had become difficult for old man Ed. His son, Eddy, helped as much as he could but he had a tow-trucking business that kept him occupied. Bob was a tremendous help. He did a lot of the day-to-day errands, running to the stores to get the parts, organizing the shop in a way that made it easy to grab the tools when needed, cleaning the rags, sweeping the floors, cleaning up miscellaneous items that were scattered around. Old man Ed did not smile much. He concentrated extremely hard on running his business, but after a while, every time he saw Bob heading his way, he broke out into a smile. Bob was a reliable worker.

"Did you go to school this week?" Old man Ed asked Bob every time he showed up for work.

"Yes, I did," Bob said.

"That's good," Ed said.

Bob never told him that he was alone, that he depended on the money he was paid to eat and buy his clothes. With the money Bob earned washing the dishes and doing brake jobs, he was collecting lots of cash that he hid in the attic of his parents' home. He dreamed of buying his own car, even building one with old parts, and he diligently saved every penny he could. He wore clean, new clothes, owned a nice coat and leather boots, and kept his hair trimmed. Only in Junior high school still, he was already a man. Steadily, he grew and filled out with pink cheeks accentuating piercing blue eyes. Every morning, he scrubbed his hands clean and took out the oil and grease from under the edges of his fingernails.

The restaurant owners started bringing Bob home to their families. Bob ate dinner with them, attended their family picnics, and was treated like one of their own.

The mothers squeezed Bob's cheeks. "You're so cute."

They made Bob feel accepted. He knew they were authentic, that this was how most families engaged with each other.

The mother pinched his arms. "You are so skinny. You need some meat on your bones. Go get yourself a plate of sausage, pasta, and bread."

Bob looked around and saw plates of food everywhere. He did not understand the names of the food - antipasto, parmesan, cannoli, but the food tasted delicious.

Through them, Bob learned that most parents deeply loved their children and treated them well. He saw that being part of a family could mean that you belonged in the world. The families fed him well, slipped him money for him to buy clothes and food, and gave him the kindness he had only known through Uncle Irving and Aunt May and his mother. Watching the way the men loved their families, how they treated their children with love and kindness affected Bob immensely. He promised himself when he grew up, he would be the kind of man whom he saw in Giovanni, Uncle Irving, Old man Ed, and the music store owners. He knew he would never be like his father. But secretly, he wished for loving relationships with his father and his brother. If they had given him a chance, he would have been a great son and a loving brother. But his father had rejected him, and his brother had not been much of a loving support for him. He knew it but, even so, struggled to accept the truth.

At the end of 7th grade, every student had to turn in a science fair project that they had developed and worked on throughout the year. Each student was required to display their project in the gymnasium for the annual science fair that all the parents and Riverside residents attended.

Bob did not need the entire grade year to invent something to do. His mind was full of ideas. All his short life, he had collected gadgets to store in his button box. Inside it was an amazing array of inventions waiting for him to construct. The best part of the science fair project was that his father would not be able to destroy his invention. Bob would be able to share it with the entire town of Riverside. Most of all, he wanted to show his teachers that he could create something special.

The month before the 7th grade science fair, Bob rummaged through his button box, intent on creating his own little mechanical masterpiece. He found an old, wind-up music box. Looking at the internal parts of it, he formulated an idea to make a special-effect light show like he had seen on the Get Smart television show and the James Bond movies. He realized he could electrify the music box drum to create a multi-colored, light show on a thin board. The metal sphere's elevated prongs provided the perfect mechanism for him to create his light display. He dug through his button box for wires and an electric outlet plug. He took a piece of plywood from his father's wood shop. At the automotive store, he bought some different colored light bulbs and mounted 30 colored light bulbs onto the sheet of plywood. The music box's forks were all different lengths. He soldered skinny wires to the plate that hit the music box's fork-ends. When he turned the crank, the tin box pinged and produced the musical tune. Then he ran wires from the other end to the lightbulbs displayed on the board. Next, he ran a grounded, black wire from the opposite end of the barrel to a battery he found in his father's wood shop. He ran a red-hot wire from the battery to the display board to complete the electrical circuit. He turned the crank attached to the music box barrels and watched what happened. The barrel turned, the wires hit the music box's circular prongs and played the tune, and the colorful lights lit up the board for a beautiful light show. Each note played caused a corresponding, colored light bulb to light up.

He worked long into the nights until the project was completed to perfection. He was thrilled with his finished project. The night before the science fair, his excitement grew. This was, in his mind, his most exciting creation. In the morning, he proudly carried his invention to the school and put it on a display table. Proudly, he printed his name. Then he grabbed a chair and sat beside his invention.

Other students set their projects up in the room too, but they put a couple of chairs around their displays because their parents wanted to proudly sit beside them and share in their child's hard work.

As the day passed, Robby's invention was visited the most by the teachers, parents, and even the other students. Everyone loved the interactive component of turning the crank to initiate the music and light display.

His English teacher put her hand on his arm and told him, "That's highly creative, Bob. I did not know you could produce something so clever."

Bob felt a twinge of happiness run from his arm straight to his heart. He rarely smiled, but now he could not stop smiling.

The judges asked Bob, "Did your father help you make the music box?"

Bob shook his head. "I made it by myself."

The judges looked skeptical. They did not seem to believe him. In the end, they told him he would win the top prize, but only after they talked to his father. Bob's win was bittersweet because he knew he would be cheated out of first place at the end when his father never arrived to confirm that Bob had made the invention on his own. But he was satisfied. For the first time in his life, someone had recognized his mechanical creations as something worthy of a first-prize trophy. That was enough for him.

The summer break brought warm breezes and made the tree leaves wrestle with nature's songs. Bob had little idle time to sit in trees and watch nature. He was busy working in the restaurant and helping old man Ed in his garage. Tinkering with cars gave Bob a sense that he was just as intelligent as the other neighborhood kids who produced good school grades for their parents every year. Bob could open the hood of a car and name each part and how each part worked together to make the magic machine drive down the road. He spent long hours under the hoods of cars. He replaced brakes, and even helped old man Ed replace an engine. He learned how to do tune-ups and change the oil. Bob became skilled and knowledgeable about car mechanics.

When Bob heard the community was hosting a soapbox derby race for the towns' children, he decided to build his own soapbox car to enter the race. The car had to be made completely out of wood and had to be made by the contestant without any parental help. Bob eagerly worked on his ideas for a derby car. His clever mind perused his father's wood shop for things he could use. He selected the sheets of plywood he needed to complete his car. He cut the wood for the body using his dad's electric saw. He went to the Zayre's department store parking lot and took two shopping carts, because their carts had the largest back wheels he could find. He pushed them home and took the two shopping carts apart, taking the wheels and the steel axels that ran between them. He built the body, pounding the nails to attach the plywood pieces to resemble a car. He nailed a plywood piece to the floor to rest his feet on while he raced. He attached the front wheels and the axel and then attached the back wheels and axel in the same manner. He made a steering device by putting an axel on a wooden pivot that steered the car. He built his own brake system by bolting a narrow, wooden two-by-four next to the driver's seat. When he pulled on it, the wood's end scraped the ground and stopped the little car. He was thrilled when he drove the car down the hill and was able to stop it within fifty feet. Using his father's red, house paint, he painted a large, white rat with its tail stretched along each side of the car.

On race day, the community parents arrived with their boys. Each brought their own soap box derby car they had made. Bob arrived alone and placed his car at the street starting line. He waited patiently as the families visited each other and admired the homemade cars. Each car was painted in bright colors, but only Bob's car had a brake system. When the attendees admired Bob's car, he enthusiastically explained how he had built the car.

When the race was about to begin, Bob stood by his car, ready to go. The whistle blew. He pushed his car, leaped into his little seat, and sped down the road. As the wind hit him, he felt a jolt of excitement race through him. The parents cheered. Swiftly, he flew, the wheels rocking and shaking him, his hands clutching the steering wheel as he strived to maintain control. He roared past the other cars and was the first to pass the finish line. He won! He pulled on his brake system and stopped his car. None of the other kids could stop their cars and flew past him until their cars slowly stopped.

To decide the final winner, they had to race three times. The best out of three won. Bob won every race.

The judges, who were the fathers of the other boys in the race, approached him.

One of them said, "Congratulations, son."

Bob stood proudly by his car and waited to be recognized and receive his ribbon.

"Where's your father?" one asked him.

"He's working," Bob said.

"Hold on," one father said.

The men left Bob and talked together in private. Bob imagined the ribbon he would receive, that everyone would clap at his amazing achievement, that he would take his 1st place ribbon and proudly display it in his attic or in his favorite treehouse in Saucony Woods. No, the attic would be better. It would be safer there and would not get damaged by the rain and no one would find it and take it.

Finally, the men approached Bob. He stood proud and tall, his hand on his steering wheel.

"We want to give you first prize," one father said, "but we want to talk to your father first to make sure you actually did make this car on your own."

"He's working in Maine," Bob said. "I wish my father had helped me, but he didn't."

"When he comes home, tell him to come by my house and talk to me. We do not really believe a boy your age could make a car this sophisticated," one of the fathers said. The three judges had children who were in the contest too.

Bob felt deflated. He knew his father would never talk to these men. His father wished him dead and hoped he would never see Bob again. Even on the occasional weekend when his father came home, Bob did not allow his father to see him even briefly. "Okay." Dejected, he took his car and pushed it toward his parents' house. Behind him, he heard a father handing out the prizes to the winners. Chuck, the boy who came in second was given the first-place prize. Upon hearing he lost the prize, Bob's shoulders slumped. The car seemed to weigh more than it did earlier. He leaned in and slowly pushed it home. At least, he had won, he told himself, even if he did not get to claim his prize.

A few weeks later, while Bob was sitting in the kitchen, his father came home. When Bob heard his father's car pull onto the driveway, he quickly raced downstairs and out the back cellar door. As soon as his father had gone into the house, Bob sprinted through the backyard and into the trees. Quickly he climbed a tree and sat camouflaged on a platform. From outside, he could not see or hear his father, mother, and two baby sisters settling back into the house. But after a while, his father came out the back door and walked around the backyard. Bob crouched down. When his father saw his soap box derby car propped up against the house, he became visibly agitated. He picked up the back end and looked at it. He dropped it on the ground. He stamped his foot. He ran his hand through his hair. Then he stormed toward the backdoor.

His mother came out onto the back porch. "What's wrong, Charles?"

"Robby used my good plywood to build that car." His father yelled. "I needed that wood for myself." He stormed into the house.

His mother walked down the porch steps and to the soapbox car. Her back to Bob, she stood looking at it for a while. Then she turned toward the back door and began walking very slowly. She rubbed her forehead. She reached for the porch railing, gripped it, and slowly stepped up the stairs. Then she went inside the house.

Bob quickly got down from the tree and sprinted to Saucony Woods to hide there. He stayed there nursing his broken heart. He lay for a long time until he was able to shake off his father's reaction to his derby car. He had worked a long time designing and building the car and was immensely proud of it. No one could take that feeling away from him. In the brief time since he had been abandoned, he had learned to harden his feelings toward his father. He told himself to focus on the positive part of their return. When his father left the house to run an errand, he would sneak home to see his mother. Feeling comforted by the thought of seeing her, he rested, dozing off for short periods. In the short span of the year, he had grown the length of his platform house. He lay on an old pillow he had taken from his mother's linen closet and embraced the solitude of nature.

After a couple of hours, he heard someone calling, "Robby! Robby!" At first it was faint, but the calling grew louder and louder.

Bob rolled over onto his stomach and peered over the platform. He was high up the tree, and the branches were so thick around him that no one would notice his tree house or him. The calling grew louder. Bob was quiet and still as he could be. He watched the ground below him. He recognized the voice. It was Nancy, his sister, the sibling who loved him and left him food at his attic door when he had been locked away. She had given him a special knock at his door so he would recognize it was her. He would open the door and she would have left him food, pencils, paper, and items to help him through the torture of being locked away. Before school every day, she had come to the attic and helped him make his old clothes look presentable. She tucked his shirts in, adjusted the buttons in a way that did not show that one was missing, pulled up his socks to cover his exposed legs. She pulled his belt straps tighter to hide his broken zipper.

Bob listened to her calling his name over and over. She was getting closer. Then he saw her, pushing her way through the thick brush, looking around the ground. She never looked up into the trees. Nancy passed by Bob, calling his name. "Robby! Robby!" But he could not answer. If he did, his hidden world would be exposed. He knew he must never reveal that he lived in the trees. His heart ached for her, but he declined to answer. He watched her make her way past him, calling his name over and over. "Robby, you can come home now," she called. He did not respond. He wanted to. He wanted to call out to her, to tell her that he was okay, that he loved her. He wanted to thank her for genuinely caring for him. But he had hardened just enough, enough to know that his self-preservation mattered most of all, above love, above sharing oneself with others. He knew because of her he would always be a good person. Only because of her was he able to survive, but that message would have to wait. If he ever gave it to her, he did not know.

CHAPTER 19

One day, on his time off work and school, Bob walked with his friend, Ralph, to the Providence River. Ralph came from an intact family, and Bob's sister, Terry, was a friend of Ralph's older sister. Ralph's family was musical, and Ralph played the drums. Bob and Ralph talked about starting a band together. But today, they just wanted to fish. Once at the river, the two budding teenagers went into Carrie's bait shop. Bob bought a Garcia Mitchell 306 rod and reel and some clam worms to fish with. They walked to the rickety bridge that crossed over the Providence River to fish at the edge of the stream. Bob had changed since he began working for Giovanni and Old Man Ed. Away from his father, he was beginning to finally recover from the numbing shock he had felt living with his family. Since he had been abandoned, he had grown, and although still thin for his height, he was beginning to look healthy. With all the money he had earned, he had bought shirts, sweaters, pants, shoes, and wore his hair neatly trimmed above his ears. He had learned to take care of all his needs.

Bob and Ralph went to the edge of the river. Bob admired the magnificent rod. He remembered all the fishing poles he had dug out of garbage cans and had brought home during the years he lived with his family. His father had callously snapped all of them in two and thrown them in the garbage. Those poles had signified his freedom. Now he owned the best fishing rod money could buy. He set the clam on the hook and dropped the line in the river. Within half an hour, Bob caught a six-pound striped bass.

"Wow!" Ralph said. "A big one."

Bob reeled it in and took the bass off the hook.

"Let me get a photo of you with it," Ralph said.

With one hand holding the reel and the other holding the fish and sporting his new blue-jean pants, his new tennis shoes, a white shirt under a sweater vest, Bob looked straight into a camera. Ralph held the camera up to snap Bob's photo holding his prize bass. Bob turned his lips upward into a slight smile. Ralph snapped the photo.

Later that day, Bob went to old man Ed Daft's garage to install new brakes on a car. The day progressed. He focused on his job. He was under a car when he heard a moan. His concern piqued. He listened. It sounded like a person was moaning. No? Some of the sounds that filtered into the shop were hard to discern. Bob decided to investigate. He quickly got out from under the car and walked toward the sound. The moans were coming from the muddy car yard behind the shop, the place where old man Ed stored his old junk cars. Feeling a sense of urgency, Bob picked up his pace. He walked around an old Ford and saw Ed's legs sticking out from under it. The jack had slipped in the mud and the car's front end had landed on top of Ed's chest.

"Hold on, Ed." Bob sprinted back to the shop, got another jack, and quickly raced back to the car. Like a madman, he placed the jack under the car and quickly began cranking up the car. When the car was elevated enough, he leaned over and with all his strength, pulled on Ed's legs. His jack began slipping. The car began falling on Ed. Just as Bob cleared Ed away from the car, the car crashed back into the mud.

Ed gave a weak cry. He lay sprawled on the ground, struggling to breathe.

"Help," Bob yelled over and over but no one came. Luck was on his side when Ed's son, Eddy, pulled up to the shop in his tow truck.

Bob ran to Eddy. "Quick! Your dad!"

He led Eddy to his father.

"Jesus," Eddy said.

Eddy lifted his father's shoulders. Bob lifted his legs. They carried him to Eddy's truck. Carefully, they lay Ed on the passenger seat. Eddy got into the truck behind the driver's wheel, turned on his rooftop lights, and sped down the street, racing toward the hospital. Bob watched the road long after they left. A whirlwind of emotions churned inside of him. He did not know what to do. He stood looking at the empty road, filled with anxiety and worry. If old man Ed died, he would never forgive himself. He walked inside the shop and paced around it until a car pulled up.

"Hello," Bob said to the man.

"I have come to pick up my car. Ed fixed it today," the man said.

Bob had not handled any of the business' paperwork, but he said, "Okay." He went to Ed's desk and went through the invoices. He found the car's invoice and saw old man Ed had detailed the work he had completed on the car. "Sign here," he said to the man.

The customer signed the form and then gave Bob his money. "The keys?"

Bob found the keys hanging on a board behind the desk and gave them to the man. Then he wrote down on the invoice that he had received the payment. The man left with his car. Not knowing where old man Ed put his payments, Bob put the money in the drawer, far in the back for safekeeping.

Bob finished his work and then locked up the shop. He went to the restaurant and washed the customers' dishes. When he was done for the night, he went to Saucony Woods, the place where he could find some inner solace and peace. He climbed onto his platform house and lay down and stared at the distant stars. He thought about the day's events. Seeing old man Ed so gravely injured hurt him more than all the punches and slaps he had ever received from his father. Bob appreciated the kindness Ed had given him. In fact, Bob loved old man Ed. And then Bob thought, if he could feel love, why didn't his father feel love? He wondered why his father hit him and did not care enough to help him. He wondered how his father could abandon him. He could not deny that his father was incapable of love. But Bob could love. He could feel sadness when someone was hurt, and if he could feel sadness, then he must be also able to feel joy and love. Looking up at the stars in the cool evening, he realized that he was not like his father and never would be. He was a person who could feel emotions for others. The realization came as a tremendous relief. He lay peacefully on his bed of leaves. He sent prayers to the sky to tell the heavens to heal old man, Ed. He let the night owls and crickets and croaking frogs be his soothing nighttime song. He let the slight breeze pass over him as if the heavens were calming him. He fell asleep.

Old man Ed was in the hospital a few days. Eddy closed the shop while his father was healing. Bob took care of Ed's two German Shepherds. Every day after school, Bob ran to the shop to walk, water, and feed them. Then at dinner time, he ran to the restaurant to wash the dishes until late in the evening. After work, he ran back to old man Ed's shop to check on the dogs. Then he went to his parents' house to sleep for the night.

Word spread through town that Bob had saved old man Ed Daft. Everyone knew. Everywhere Bob went his shoulders were slapped, his hand shook, and Bob felt proud he had saved his friend, old man, Ed, one of his greatest teachers and mentors.

A few days later, while Bob sat inside his parents' house at the kitchen table, he heard his parents' car pull into the driveway. Bob immediately stood and headed into the cellar. By the time he opened the cellar door to the outside, he heard his family going into the kitchen. He had left dirty dishes in the sink, the garbage full, but as he disappeared around the block, he did not care. He was safe. He made his way to Saucony Woods and snuck into the woods through his friend's broken backyard fence. He walked through the thick woods to the tree where his platform house was. He climbed up the old maple tree and rested high on his tiny home. He lay down and looked at all the tree branches intertwining above him. The leaves wrestled. The birds sang. Ants crawled along the tree trunk. It was a rare day off for Bob, and he needed some rest. Despite his parents surprising him with a sudden visit home, he had nothing to worry about. His father could no longer touch him. He was free. He missed his mother but someday, when they finished building their cabins in Maine, they would come home permanently, and he could visit with her while his father was at work. He wished he had his guitar, but he had left it in the attic. How fun it would be to sit in his little treehouse and play his guitar. He had gotten quite good and was playing with some of the neighborhood kids in town. His pocket was full of cash and in the attic, he had stashed his money. He loved counting his money. It would not be long before he would be able to buy his own car. Being free from his father's wrath had given him an opportunity to be a good friend to his classmates and the neighborhood kids. Best of all, he had earned the respect of the town when he saved old man Ed Daft from being crushed by the car.

Old man Ed returned to the shop. He could manage some of the physical labor of the car repairs, but he relied on Bob to do the heavier physical work, especially the heavy lifting and any work that needed to be done underneath the car.

One day, while Bob was preparing to do a brake job at the shop, old man Ed came over by him and sat on a bench. While he was recovering, his son, Eddy, had managed the account books and all was in order. Old man Ed was not only relieved but also grateful. Bob had proven himself far beyond what he thought he was capable of, and he was proud.

"You have a knack for working on cars," old man Ed told him. "My son does too, and he's good with the books."

Bob stood by an old Chevy, wiping his hands on a rag to clean them. "What are you getting at?"

Old man Ed took a deep breath. "Just saying, my future is in good hands, I believe."

"That so?" Bob put the rag down and disappeared under the hood of the chevy with his wrench. For a moment, they were silent. Bob contemplated what old man Ed had said. Was this garage his future? He was still just a kid and hadn't thought about what he would be as an adult. He had never thought beyond living in his treehouses, scrounging to survive. He always believed he belonged to the natural forces of the earth, high in the trees, letting the wind, the rain, the sun, and the snow be a part of his daily living, fishing for his food, catching crawdads in the creeks to eat, getting free meals from Giovanni's restaurant. To think he would have to plan beyond that had never occurred to him. The only dream he cultivated at night while lying in the trees, watching the moon and stars peeking through the black silhouette of the thick branches, was to own his own car. He imagined driving down the road in his souped-up old chevy, feeling as free as the birds that flew.

"I don't think I thanked you properly for saving my life," old man Ed said.

Bob continued to work. "No need to thank me. I am the one who should be thanking you."

That night, Bob lay in the Saucony woods tree house and dreamed of the car he would someday own. He lay for a long time, resting, dozing off for short periods, and embracing the solitude of nature. For the first time in his life, he believed he would make it. Hope had somehow, against all odds, found him.

CHAPTER 20

By the time Bob entered 8th grade, he had already spent an entire year living on his own. He attended school every day and worked for old man Ed and Giovanni. At the restaurant, the Italian cooks taught him all their secret sauce recipes. The secret was in adding the ingredients a little at a time, letting the sauce simmer to perfection. Bob learned how to make meatballs to go with the sauces, how to cook the pasta exactly right and pour the sauce on the pasta, add the large pork meatballs, and sprinkle them with parmesan cheese. He enjoyed the pasta meals so much that he did not bother to go to McDonalds or all the other fast-food restaurants that were cropping up in the neighborhood. While walking along the street, if his stomach rumbled for food, he knew just the place to go for good company and great food. Always welcomed and given a free meal, Bob found Giovanni, his family, his friends, his cooks, and table-waiters to be the family he always wanted. He kept his promise and did not smoke or drink, went to school every day, and listened to his teachers.

His mother had left her Ford Fairlane in the driveway. The keys were in the house inside a small desk locker. Bob made a copy of the key and kept it for himself. He often took the car out around the block and taught himself to drive. Within a couple of months, he was a skilled driver. The best part was that the neighbors were not paying attention to the fact that he was driving.

During Bob's earlier years, his older sister, Terry, had let Bob hang around with her and her friends. They took Bob to concerts. At outdoor, summer concerts, her male friends hoisted Bob onto their shoulders so he could have the best view of the concert. Once they took Bob to the Newport Folk Festival to see the concert. Bob was mesmerized by the bands and the music. After the show, the artists came out to the crowd. Bob met Bob Dylan and Joan Baez. He was completely captivated by the music.

When Terry's male classmates graduated high school, they either became local police officers or were drafted into the army. Terry went to college but stayed connected with her high school friends. All the boys finished their draft requirements and came back to Riverside within several months of each other. To pass the time, they spent time together in Freddy's garage, sitting on crates, and drinking whiskey. All eight of the veterans had become addicted to amphetamines while fighting in Vietnam. On his days off, Bob hung around with them in the garage, sometimes all night. There was a hole in the garage door that Bob slipped through to get inside to visit them. He listened to them talk. They sent Bob on booze errands for them. Bob ran to the Italian restaurants to buy the whiskey for the boys. All the Italian restaurant owners were sympathetic to the Vietnam vets and accommodated their liquor requests. Bob also knew a guy who would sell him Dexedrine, or dexies, or black beauties, as the guys called it. Bob brought the pills back to the traumatized veterans.

One of the guys, Steve, did one tour in Vietnam, came home, married his longtime girlfriend, and then signed up to do another tour. In Vietnam, it rained for two months straight, and Steve had to trudge through the wet rice paddies. He wore his boots without socks. A foot sore became infected from the dampness inside his boot. The infection traveled up his leg to his thigh, and then became gangrene. The doctors amputated his leg. He returned home disabled. Sitting in the garage with the other veterans, he complained continuously that his amputated leg itched.

"My foot itches awfully bad," he said.

"Stevie, you don't have a leg to scratch," the other guys told him and then laughed.

"Don't mess with me," Steve said. "My damn foot itches."

"How can something itch that's not there," Butchy said.

Steve looked irritated. "Get over here, Robby, and scratch my toes."

"Not possible," Butch said.

Bob felt sorry for Stevie. If his foot itched, it itched, even if it was not there. He knelt before Steve and removed his pretend boot. He set it beside him. Then he pretended to scratch Steve's phantom toes.

Steve put his head back and sighed in relief. He giggled and laughed. "It feels so good! You are doing a fantastic job, Robby."

Bob scratched and scratched at nothing, pretending to relieve the itch in his phantom foot and toes. When Bob was done, he sat back down in the corner and resumed listening to the guys talk. Bob was dedicated to the Vietnam veterans. Before the neighborhood gang had been shipped to Vietnam they had been surfing in the ocean, racing cars, acting like the cool teenagers they were, but they changed when they arrived home. Now they were ragged and hairy and sloppily dressed. They were outcasts in the neighborhood. But they had taken Bob right in, which pleased Bob immensely. Over time, Bob noticed that Tim was their leader, and all the guys followed him.

One evening, the Vietnam veterans left the garage and went to town to Riverside Square, where the four corners met. Bob tagged along. The pizza restaurant, the corner bar, and the market provided the perfect place for them to gather and talk under the streetlights, drink beer, and smoke cigarettes. They slugged beers and talked for hours. Although the police and the veterans had been friends in high school, the police now sided with society against the Vietnam vets. Two police cars pulled up at the corner. They got out of their cars. It was clear by their expressions they were not happy with the veterans loitering at the corner. The police officers and the vets exchanged heated words.

"Get off the street corner," the police officers told the veterans.

"We ain't doing nothing wrong. We're just talking. It's legal to walk down the street," Tim told the police officers.

"You're disturbing the people who are here to do legitimate business," the police officers said.

Tim laughed. "Who are we disturbing?" He clenched his fists. "You don't have any right to tell us war vets here, after fighting for our country, that we can't stand on a corner street."

"You cops would never survive in a war zone. Just stupid cowards you all are." Butchy Flowers went to the police officer, his old high school friend, and shoved him.

The police officer shoved him back. Immediately, the rest reacted. Flying fists ensued. On the corner, a small melee between young men in police uniforms and veterans with long hair and sloppy, loose clothing broke out. Bob stood by the building and watched the fighting. Mistakenly, an officer had left the engine running in his car and their door open. Butchy Flowers jumped into one of the police cars and took off in it down the street, driving at high speed, burning rubber and blaring the sirens. The police officers and veterans stopped pushing each other and watched Butchy flying around in the police car. The veterans laughed. The police officers did not try to stop him. They stood helplessly as Butchy taunted them. Eventually, Butchy stopped the car. He got out of the car and slammed the door. The veterans walked back to Freddie's garage, laughing all the way. Bob followed them back to the garage, and they spent the night laughing at how they had outfoxed the cops.

Mr. Fischer came into old man Ed's auto shop to have the brakes replaced on his car. He stayed and watched Bob replace his brakes. Bob, at only 13 years old, could accurately change brake systems in a timely manner. "I'm impressed," he said to Bob. "For being so young, you're quite a good mechanic."

Bob leaned out from under the car. "Thanks."

"You're friends with my daughters, Faith and Hope?"

"Yes, sir, I am," Bob said.

"I have an old gray '57 Chevy sitting in my driveway that I was thinking of giving to my daughters, but they won't be able to drive for a few more years. Would you like it?" he said to Bob.

"That would be nice, Mr. Fischer. I would give anything to have a car like that."

"That's so?" Mr. Fischer said. "It needs a lot of fixing to get it back to where it originally was."

"I'd fix it right up. I would get it running," Bob said.

"I tell you what," the man said, "for $75.00 you can have it."

"Really?" Bob said.

"Really," the man said.

"I can bring you the money tomorrow," Bob said. He would have to get the money out of the attic at his parents' house, but he had more than enough for the car.

"Aren't you too young to be driving?" Mr. Fischer asked.

"Yes, but I love cars, and I'd love to be able to tinker with them in my spare time," Bob told him.

"Then it is yours. Come by my house tomorrow to pick it up and pay me then." Mr. Fischer said.

Bob shook his hand. "I'll take good care of it."

The next day Bob took the money over to Mr. Fischer's house. He knocked on his door and when Mr. Fischer answered, he gave him the money. They walked to the driveway where the old 1957 chevy sat on the gravel driveway. Bob was overcome with emotion. He was only 13 and he owned his first car.

"I'll drive it to your driveway," Mr. Fischer said.

Bob hopped into the front passenger seat and shut the door. Mr. Fischer got into the driver's seat, started the engine, and slowly drove the car as it popped and sputtered and expelled exhaust to Bob's parent's house, two blocks away. Bob knew the car needed a lot of work. Mr. Fischer pulled it into the driveway, drove it up near the house, stopped the engine, and got out of the car.

"Enjoy your new car, son," Mr. Fischer said.

Bob smiled so wide that the skin around his lips tightened. He had never felt so happy, so exhilarated, so bubbly. He had his first car! And he was not even legally able to drive. "Thank you," He shook Mr. Fischer's hand like a man would.

Mr. Fischer laughed. "Now remember, you can't drive it, but I'm sure you'll love tinkering with it."

"I will." Bob watched Mr. Fischer walk down his driveway and turn toward his house two blocks down. When he was out of sight, Bob got into the driver's seat and started the engine. He backed it down the driveway and onto the street. He drove his new car around the block. In the past year, he had grown so much his feet reached the gas and brake pedals. As he drove, none of the neighbors noticed him or thought anything out of the ordinary when they saw the car go by their house. Bob was on top of the world. But he could tell that it was going to be a lot of work to get the car running right. He drove it to his parents' house and parked it.

In his spare time, he customized the car's interior and exterior. The Chevy's exterior was green and white, but he carefully painted it black with house paint. Inside the car, he tacked black and white, zebra-striped shag carpet on the walls, floor, and dashboard. He even tacked it onto the ceiling. There were no door handles or knobs on the old car, but inside his button box, he found toilet flush-handles, sink-faucet handles, and oven heater controls. He decided to install them in the dash. He installed toilet flush handles for door handles. The car radio turned on and off with stovetop knobs. He used doorknobs to work the windows up and down. The entire interior was fortified with bits of miscellaneous items he found at the junkyard.

His friends called his car "the stove" but jealous Freddie called it to the toilet. All Bob's friends loved the car. Bob took them cruising around.

While driving the car around the neighborhood, he took the license plates off his mother's car and temporarily posted them on his car. He did not go far, just to gas-up or stop at the car-parts store or up to the store to get food. When he got home, he put the license plates back on his mom's car. All year, when the weather permitted, he worked in the car. He replaced the brakes. He bought the owner's manual and read it. He decided to rebuild the engine using parts from old man Ed's junk yard. Little by little, he worked on it, following the instructions. taking out the old engine and replacing it with a more powerful engine. Bob found a stack of his father's auto mechanics magazine in the cellar shop. He spent most of his free time reading the magazine. He gained most of his mechanical knowledge from the magazine.

Bob could not get the car to run right with the new engine. Finally, he walked over to Terry's friends to enlist their help. Jeff, Tommy, and Razz owned two gas stations across from each other on a major intersection in town. They owned a lot of muscle and drag racing cars. Bob perused the cars parked in the back of the gas stations.

"Tommy approached him. "Hey kid. What you want?"

Jeff came up beside him. "That's Terry's little brother. You know, Mayhem's son, the one who tagged along with us to concerts."

Bob approached them.

Tommy peered at Bob. After a moment, he said. "Yes, you are. You grew, little kid."

"You need something?" Jeff wiped his hands on a towel.

"I need a carburetor," Bob said.

"A carburetor?" Tommy said. "I thought you were going to ask me for food." He laughed.

"I can pay you," Bob said.

"All right. Come on in," Tommy said.

Bob followed them to the back of the gas station. Tommy went to the back and brought out a used carburetor. "Here you go."

"How much?" Bob asked.

Tommy waved his hand in a dismissive manner. "You can have it for free."

"Thank you." Bob carefully carried the precious carburetor home. Immediately, he installed it in the '57 chevy. But he needed more parts. He went back and asked them for a manifold.

Tommy put his hand on his hips. "What are you doing? Why do you need a manifold?"

"I have a 57 chevy, and I'm building a V8 engine."

"You? You're just a kid," Tommy said.

Bob shrugged. He thought of himself as an adult.

"Come on." Tommy waved him in and found a manifold on a shelf. He gave it to Bob. "I'm coming by your house to see this car you got."

A week later, Tommy came by to look at the car. Bob was under the hood, tinkering with it.

"I like your car," Tommy said.

"Thanks," Bob said, looking up at him.

"How much work on this car did you do?" he asked Bob.

"I rebuilt the engine and put it into the car. Now I am trying to add the external components," Bob said.

Tommy looked under the hood. 'Good job. What did you adjust your valves to?"

"I didn't," Bob said.

"You have to set up the carburetor and the distributor right."

"I'm not sure how to do that," Bob said.

Tommy got out from under the hood. "I tell you what. I will be by in a week with the parts. I will get your car running."

One week later, six cars showed up in Bob's driveway. They were all Terry's friends from the garage. They got out of their '55 and '56 Chevys and looked at Bob's car.

"Man! Where did you get this?" Razz said. "All of us want a '57 chevy. We haven't found one."

Bob was surprised to see all the older guys. "Mr. Fischer sold it to me."

"He did," Razz said. "Well, I'll be…"

They looked under Bob's hood to see what they needed to do.

"You have to adjust the carburetor this way," Tommy said.

Razz showed him how to professionally install the distributor and get it working.

Jeff set the valves. "Where's the battery?"

"It's dead," Bob said.

'Hold on." Jeff jumped into his car, drove off, and a half hour later, came back with a battery. He installed it. Within a couple of hours, they got Bob's car running. They laughed as they revved the engine.

"Can't believe Terry's little kid brother did this." Tommy laughed.

"This car runs as good as our cars do." Jeff laughed too.

"Kid, you come by any time with your car, and we'll help you out," Razz said.

"I'll be back." Tommy got into his car and drove off. Fifteen minutes later, he arrived back with a case of beer. The group stood around and drank beer for the rest of the afternoon, talking about cars and the races they had been in, laughing and joking with each other. When they were done, the guys jumped back into their cars and spun off down the road. Bob stood watching them drive away. He was happy. Best of all, his car drove like a dream now.

A week later, Bob put his mother's license plate on his Chevy and drove it to the gas stations to show his new friends. On the street corner, he punched the gas and revved the engine. Then he loudly spun the wheels around the corner. The guys looked up from their work, smiled, and waved at him. From then on, the guys started dropping off better components, better racing parts, an aluminum manifold and a bigger carburetor. They gave him mag wheels.

"Don't sell the wheels" they told Bob. "Give them back to us if you don't use them."

To pay them back for their help, Bob went to the gas station and helped them. He ran errands for them and cleaned their shops for them. He started going with the guys on Friday and Saturday nights to the local A&W Root Beer drive-in, where they ate hamburgers and drank milk shakes. He went with them to the car rallies. Bob met Mr. Tasca, the biggest race-car enthusiast in all of Rhode Island. Mr. Tasca drove his Mustangs around town. Bob was thrilled just to be in the presence of this important man.

When Bob's new friends drove their cars around together, they let Bob go with them. The police never stopped Bob for underage driving because the guys put Bob's Chevy in the middle of their 8-car pack, so he would be ensconced in their protection. No adult was paying attention.

Bob joined the group on weekend nights when they went drag racing on Wampanoag Trail Road. Late at night, he met them at the starting line at the entrance to old Leonard's farm to watch the car enthusiasts race their cars along the road. The screaming engines, the blaring lights, the sound of screeching tires, and the wild racing down the street woke Leonardo up. But he never complained.

At the end of 8th grade, Bob had to enter another science fair project for the junior high fair. He had spent so much time working on his car that he had neglected to think of something he could display. If he had a good presentation, he may just pass through to the next grade. His teachers had long since given up requiring him to turn in his homework. Bob had become less and less interested in school, and if not for the promises he had made to Giovanni, he would have dropped out by now. He did not know any 13-year-old school dropouts, and the last thing he needed was for his father to find out he was neglecting school. The week before the science fair he found his mother's discarded vacuum cleaner. He was aware that cigarette smoking was unhealthy. His teachers had discouraged the students from ever starting to smoke. Looking at the vacuum cleaner, he developed a plan to show the dangers of smoking. If there was one thing Bob had learned from working on cars, it was the order of disassembly. To know how to take things apart was just as important as putting things back together. He plugged the vacuum in and devised a plan to make the vacuum smoke a cigarette. He connected a suction hose to the end of the vacuum cleaner, turned on the motor, and held a cigarette in front of it. The vacuum cleaner smoked an entire cigarette in a minute. He had found his science project. He wanted his automatic cigarette smoking machine to show the full amount of nicotine and tar that collects when only one cigarette is smoked and when an entire pack is smoked. He mounted and screwed the vacuum cleaner to a board. At the suction end, he made a receptacle to hold the cigarette and a place to put filters. He cut an old T-shirt into squares and stretched it over a suction hose's metal square and secured it in place. He had made a makeshift smoking machine. He placed the cigarette in front of the T-shirt and turned on the vacuum cleaner. The suction hose smoked the cigarette and collected the nicotine on the cloth filters he had installed. He removed the filter to see the amount of tar a cigarette produced in the lungs. Then he secured an entire pack of cigarettes to the cigarette receptacle and lit the cigarettes. When the vacuum had smoked all the cigarettes, he looked at the amount of tar an entire pack produced. For each pack smoked, a tablespoon of tar was produced. The tar was as thick as peanut butter.

The day of the science fair, Bob brought his smoking machine to the gymnasium. He spent the entire day showing the students, teachers, and parents the amount of tar collected in the lungs from cigarette smoking. His display was the most viewed and talked about.

His science teacher approached him and put his hand on Bob's shoulder. "Good job." He looked at Bob and smiled. "You're a hands-on kind of kid."

Bob did not know exactly what he meant. All he knew was that he had learned to invent many things. It started with the button box his mother had given him to keep him quiet in the house. His ability to create amazing things out of nothing but junk had given him a lifeline. "Thank you."

Again, the judges wanted to know if Bob's father had built the machine.

"No, I did it by myself," Bob insisted.

The judges did not believe him.

"My father doesn't help me with anything," Bob finally told them.

They awarded him first prize. His parents never found out about the invention he had made from his mother's vacuum cleaner. He passed 8th grade.

CHAPTER 21

Bob drove his Chevy all over. No one stopped him. The chief of police, who never forgot that Bob had been the kid who had brought his injured son home on a sled all those years earlier, ignored Bob's driving without a license. But the other police did not. Bob teased them. If he saw a police car, he pulled over to the side of the road, turned off the car engine, took the key out, and hid it under the seat. He slid over on the passenger side. When the police officer pulled up beside him, Bob reached over to the driver's side and rolled the window down.

"Why are you driving a car?" the police officer said.

Bob looked around as if searching for the person whom the question was addressed to. "Who me? I'm only a kid. I don't drive."

"I know you are driving. I saw you drive," the police officer said, looking irritated.

Bob stretched his arm across the back of his seat and tried to look casual.

"I know it is you. If I catch you driving, I am going to take you in," the police officer said. He shook his head and drove off.

Bob laughed. He knew who his friends in town were, and the chief-of-police was one of them.

Bob's brother, Darin, gave Bob his 1961 ford van because it did not run well. A deep green color, it looked like a giant metal box on four wheels with a flat front that placed Bob right up on the street when he drove it. The large steering wheel made him feel like he was maneuvering a city bus when he drove it. Bob was thrilled to get it. He spent hours in the back of his parents' house working on the van. When he needed a part, he went to the junkyard and pulled the part he needed from an old van that had been totaled in an accident but still had some working parts Bob could use. Over time, he had bought all the tools he needed to work on his van and spread them out on the grass, grabbing the ones he needed and working diligently, twisting screws, pulling out old parts and replacing them. He recovered old tires from the junk yard and put them in the van. He started the engine. It sputtered and coughed. He eased it out of the driveway and drove it to the Zayre store. He bought a large piece of leopard-spotted, cheap, roll-up carpet and threw it into the back of the van. Back at his parents' house, he tacked the carpet on the van floor, along the walls, and finally to the ceiling. His van was complete. He drove it around the neighborhood and past his friends' houses, beeping his horn. One by one, his friends came out, Frankie, Johnny, Stu, Bruce, and Dave, hopped in the van with him. Frankie turned the radio on with one of Bob's makeshift oven knobs, and they listened to the radio station play the Beach Boys Good Vibrations on high volume. The song blasted out the window, their arms stretched out the windows, their hands slapping the cool breeze. Bob, only 14, was already a skilled driver. He hit the road going out of Riverside toward Boston. He knew the way after being dumped there by his father many times. He sped along the expressway for miles and finally turned around and headed back home to Riverside to drop his friends off one by one, then drove to his parents' house, parked the van, crawled in the back, and slept in it. He was the neighborhood king-of-the-van.

Bob bought another car from a neighbor and fixed it up behind his parents' house. He replaced the broken parts with junkyard parts and put used tires on it, then sold it for a couple thousand dollars. He began buying old cars from people who told him the cars did not run. Bob fixed them. If the transmission or engine needed to be replaced, Bob got one from the junk yard. To hoist the blown engine out of the car, Bob made a chain fall with a series of pulleys attached to it and hoisted it over a branch of a maple tree on his parents' front lawn. He attached the chain to the engine and pulled it up with a pulley. He got every old car he bought running smoothly and then sold them for more than he bought them.

Bob bought a 1961 white Ford convertible from his sister, Nancy's boyfriend, that he drove around town. Bob also bought 3 large shipping crates with motorcycle parts. The combined parts were three complete motorcycles disassembled. He hid them behind the trees in his parents' backyard for safe keeping. In the future, he planned to build a motorcycle. But for now, he had his own car business, buying broken-down cars, fixing them, and selling them. He was making money that he stashed in his parents' attic. All cash. He was set.

Bob forged his parents' signature on a job application and got a job at the Crescent Park amusement center. The owner of the amusement park liked Bob because he showed up on time, worked for as long as they asked him to, and was very responsible at maintaining the public's safety. The owner asked Bob if he knew how to shoot a gun.

"No, sir," Bob said, a bit surprised by the question. "Why?"

"I have the shooting gallery game," he said, pointing toward the area. "It takes extra alertness and skill to run that arcade game. You seem responsible enough."

"I'd love to manage that game." As much as Bob loved working at the most impressive carousel on the east coast, he was tired of loading kids on and off it and making sure they were secured into their seats properly. The same organ music playing over and over seemed to have invaded every sleeping dream he had.

"Come with me and I'll show you," the owner said.

Bob followed him to the arcade game. From the moment Bob saw the game, he wanted to run it. For the next two hours, his boss instructed Bob how to run the game. The shooter had to hit a moving row of ducks to win a prize. The 22 caliber rifles were already secured to the front counter by chains that limited the player's ability to shoot in any direction other than the ducks on the moving chain. He took the money from the players and then let them choose which gun they wanted to use to shoot the ducks. Each shooter got fifteen shots. The more ducks the players shot, the bigger the prize they received.

Bob quickly learned and then began running the game. The owner watched him for an hour to make sure Bob could manage the job, and when he felt confident in Bob's ability, he left Bob on his own. Bob thought he had scored the best job in all of Riverside, and he was only 14 years old. For a month Bob ran the arcade shooting range, handing out prizes to the best shooters, and collecting money in a chest hidden under the counter.

Burt Sugarman, a music producer, planned to use the attached Alhambra Ballroom to host a series of concerts called the Sugarberry Lounge Concerts. He planned to host current, popular music. Burt went to the amusement park manager and said he needed stagehands to help him run his concerts. He wanted to know if the manager had any young men whom he could trust and could handle the job. Bob was referred. Burt came to watch Bob run the arcade. Bob had matured at an early age, both emotionally and physically. With a mustache and a slight goatee on his chin, no one would guess he was only 14 years old. Burt hired him on the spot. When Bob's shift was done at the arcade, Mr. Burt took him inside the Alhambra Ballroom and showed him around. The ballroom was uniquely crafted. The dark wooden, waxed floor shone. The liquor bar stretched along the entire side of the ballroom. A large glass mirror was mounted behind it, reflecting the liquor bottles lined along the bar. Patrons sat on the bar stools. Three large, red glass, shimmering chandeliers hung along the ceiling. At the ballroom's end was a large stage. Bob admired the room's magnificent presentation.

Burt Sugarman trained Bob and several of the other young men who were chosen for the job. Bob tackled it with eagerness and a willingness to work hard. First, he went to Zayre's department store and bought black leather boots with Cuban heels, black slacks, and a tuxedo shirt. He had to dress the part. The Alhambra Ballroom was a place where famous bands played. The bands were eager to play there. Burt liked Bob because Bob did everything Burt asked of him. He put Bob in charge of managing the stage, getting the equipment set up, and the instruments tuned. Bob marked large Xs on the stage for the players and the equipment. He ran the cables into the amplifiers. He got the food and drank the band requested. Bob spent his evenings backstage with the stars. He did not buy into the star-struck trance that the other hired boys did. He focused on doing his job. There was plenty of free food around and a sofa to sleep on in the back room. Bob got paid $5.00 an hour, but it was not the money that drew him in. He was drawn in by the magic of the place, the musicians, and the energy of the people that inspired him to do his best.

Burt gave Bob the job of taking care of the Three Stooges' needs when they came to perform at Sugarberries. As a kid, Bob's father had forbidden him to watch the Three Stooges show and would threaten to poke Bob in the eyes if he caught him watching it. Bob loved the three stooges and did everything they asked of him for the five days they were in town doing a live act on the stage. He got their food. He secured their hotel room. He got their beer and cigars by going to the stores of people who knew him. In real life, the three stooges were constantly joking and were always poking fun at each other. Curly loved his cigars, and they all loved their liquor. They were hilarious and entertained Bob backstage before their show began.

Burt took his concert series on the road. He took Bob with him. Everyone knew Burt had this kid with him who did everything Burt asked. Bob was backstage with the stars - the Ojs, Spinners, and the Temptations. Mostly Burt promoted all of Barry Gordy's bands. Bob loved working with them all, especially The Left Banke.

Bob's started 9th grade with renewed confidence and pride in his abilities. By then, he was schooled in managing band concerts. And having the Alhambra Ballroom to sleep in had given him an entire summer free of sleeping at his parents' house and running to the treehouses when his parents made a surprise weekend trip home from Maine.

In 9th grade, his last year of Jr. High school, Bob could not keep up with his classes. His focus was on his car, his jobs, and his friends. At old man Ed Daft's shop, Bob was doing four brake jobs every day. Then at night, he went to the Alhambra Ballroom to help Mr. Sugarman or, if he could, to Giovanni's restaurant to help wash dishes. By the time he was done it was late, and he got little sleep before it was time to attend school. But he had made his promise to Giovanni and his family that he would attend school – and no drinking, no smoking, and no trouble. During the weekend days, he rebuilt old cars and sold them. At only 14 years old, he was making a lot of money, which was stored in his parents' attic.

Bob attended every day like the restaurant owners had insisted, but he was not committed to learning. He never completed his homework. The tactic he had used at home, remaining invisible and silent, seemed to work for him at school too. But his English teacher, Mrs. Smith, watched him daily in class. One day, she called him to her desk after class was dismissed. As the other students exited the classrooms to go to their next class, Robby quietly walked to Mrs. Smith's desk and stood to the side of it, his hands in his pockets, wondering if he was in trouble for something. He had completed his classroom work to the best of his ability, although he was aware that his classroom work was not up to the more advanced level of his classmates. A good talking to was nothing like a slap on the back of his head, but he did not want to hear that he was flunking or that he would have to bring his father in to talk to his teacher. At least, he told

himself, he looked respectable. With the money he had
made, he had bought all new school clothes, new pants, new
shirts, a leather belt, and new shoes, and if nothing else,
standing in front of the teacher, he looked clean and proper.
He took a deep breath and told himself that if he had to drop
out of school for failing, at least he would have a job.

But Mrs. Smith looked at him and smiled. She sat
erect at her desk with her hands folded on her neatly stacked
papers. Behind her on the chalkboard she had written the
relevant points of the story they had read the night before for
homework. Only Bob had not read the story, but to his
credit, he had sat quietly and listened to Mrs. Smith's
interpretation of the story for their classroom discussion that
day. She was young, with dark curly hair and big brown eyes.
"I have something important to talk to you about," she said.
"I see you are not doing your homework and not
participating in our class discussions. I have graded you on
some of your classroom work and I must say, you have
potential."

Bob did not respond, except to put his hands in his
pocket and shuffle his feet.

"I have a suggestion that I think will work, Bob. You
like to be called Bob, right?"

"Yes," Bob spoke up.

"Instead of doing homework and the classroom work,
I'm going to give you a journal." Mrs. Smith reached into
her desk and pulled out a binder. She did not give it to Bob
but held it up for him to see. "Every day, you must draft a
story during class time. At the end of the class, I want you to
turn it in to me. I will keep it stored on my desk for you to
pick up at the start of every class. I want to hear your stories,

Bob. If you come to class every day and write in your journal, I will grade you solely on your journal and not on the homework or classroom work. In other words, you no longer must do the required classroom work. Is that all right with you?"

"Yes," Bob said. "I can do that." Relief washed over him. He relaxed.

"You can go now," she said. "Do not forget our agreement. You must come to class every day and write in your journal."

"I will." Bob turned and left the room. He always kept his promises, and he was also full of stories that he could write about in the journal.

At first, Bob drafted fictional stories in his journal, but as the year passed, he mixed his stories with some of his real-life issues. He told his teacher about the woods where he lived in the trees. He told her about the attic in his parents' house where he had been confined to live without heat in the winter and stifling heat in the summer months. He told her about fishing in the ponds for food. He told her about his jobs at the restaurant, about working for old man Ed in his auto shop. He told her about his cleaning job at the music shop, how he had become very skilled on the guitar, that they had given him free guitar lessons, and how he had practiced in the attic. He told her about his Uncle Irving and Aunt May's farm in Nova Scotia and how he had learned from his Uncle Irving how to survive in the woods on his own. He went into detail on how he was able to catch fish from streams just by using his hand. In each story he wrote to her, he felt some of the weight he was carrying was being lifted off him as if, for the first time, he was letting someone else into his secret life.

In addition, he shared the stories he had told to the neighborhood children with his shadow puppet theatre. The stories were always about good versus evil. When he made up characters and placed them into life and death situations, he always resolved the issues by bringing in an outside character who would rid the story of its evil and restore the good characters to good lives.

For her part, Mrs. Smith corrected the misspellings, the bad grammar, and the punctuation mistakes. This helped Bob's writing tremendously, but most of all, he grew to love going to his English class where he could for the first time express his life to someone. Best of all, Bob knew he was her favorite student. She began referring to Bob in class as their class philosopher, and in that way, Bob felt special. None of the other kids thought to challenge the teacher on the special standards she graded Bob's classroom work or the fact that he never had homework to turn in. Since Bob was the classroom's special philosopher, the kids knew he was somehow special, at least that is what Bob believed.

One day, Mrs. Smith said to the class, "Today, we are going to do something different. Our philosopher, Bob, is going to go around to each of you students and whisper in your ear the start of your story. Then you finish the story."

When the teacher told Bob to start, he stood, went to one student, and whispered, "You see a UFO in a park. The beings come out of it. Are they good or bad?" Then he went to the next student and whispered, "You are in a moving elevator, and it suddenly stops, and the lights go out. You are trapped. What happens next?" Then to the next student, he whispered, "You are riding in a car, and it spins out on the street. What happens next?" When Bob was done, he sat back down and authored his own story. He started with "I am in the woods, and I am lost…. He wrote three pages by the end of the class.

The stories that the classroom wrote were featured in the junior high newspaper. They created a lot of interest among the teachers, the parents, and the students. Bob was incredibly happy to be recognized for his creative writing ideas. But in truth, his grades no later mattered to him. His father no longer smacked him when he gave his father his report card, so he had nothing to fear, nor did he really need school. He was surviving fine on his own terms without an education.

Bob did not keep up with his classes that year. Finally, the school decided to have Bob repeat his 9th grade. That meant he would not be going to high school for another year. All his classmates graduated and went on to high school. Bob spent the graduation day in Saucony Woods in his treehouse, lying on his back and staring into the tree branches whose leaves were wrestling in the cool wind. He wished he did not care about being held back a grade, but he did. In the end, it did not matter. He was on his way upward in life, heading forward, working, and completely self-sufficient.

The neighborhood kids loved the current music. All the boys wanted to be musicians. Many garage bands sprung up in Riverside. Over time, Bob began playing an electric bass guitar. Bob joined a garage band. Ralph was the drummer in his band. John was the lead guitar player. Gordon was the organist. The popular songs on the radio were easy to play because they followed the basic three-chord-changes with four-time beats. They practiced in Ralph's garage, blasting the songs into the street. Ralph's father set up a stage for the boys in his garage and supported his son's desire to be in a rock band. The neighborhood kids gathered. Thye sat politely in the grass to listen to them rehearse. The band practiced on Sundays and learned enough songs to be hired to play at the Jr. High weekend dances. They called themselves, "The Uproars."

Their first night, they walked onto the stage full of confidence and bravado. Most of all, they felt empowered by the music they were playing, energized by their new budding sexual desires that would go unfulfilled for a while. They played all their songs like pros, the girls dancing in groups together, occasionally bringing a shy male in from the sidelines to dance with them. The energy pulsated to the drumbeat. At the ceiling, a ball spun around, sending colored lights racing around the dark room. The chaperoning teachers stood off to the side, talking to each other, ignoring the teens and the band. When the night was done, The Uproars felt they had met one of their most significant teenage achievements. They had become a neighborhood band.

The band wanted to trade Bob for another band player because the other player had a bigger amplifier. Bob's amplifier was small and did not generate enough sound on stage. Bob needed a bigger amplifier. They were expensive. He decided to buy a powerful heath-kit amplifier for two hundred dollars. It came in a kit that he would have to assemble, but he had gotten good at fixing cars and believed he could build his own amplifier too. He brought it to his father's wood shop. When he opened it, he realized it was going to be complicated to build. It came in an empty amplifier case and had a thin board with a channel system built in, an electrical solid-state circuit board, a bag of cathodes, diodes, and resisters. The pieces looked like aspirin with two little wires sticking out of them. He spent hours figuring out where each little electrical circuit was connected to. He had to solder the wire circuits very delicately to a circuit board.

When he was finally done, he took it to the Uproars dance show and brought it onstage. At first, the other band members laughed at him. But when Bob began to play, the sound was phenomenal, and everyone stopped and listened. Bob knew even adults had a challenging time putting the kit together, but he had completed it with relative speed and accuracy. He kept his band job.

Ralph's sister, Mary, was dating a drummer, Dino Danelli, of the famous, current rock band, The Rascals. The Rascals had records on the radio. Every day, Bob listened to It's a Beautiful Morning, People Got to be Free, and Grooving on the airways. The Rascals were idolized by every garage band in Rhode Island, up the Jersey coast, and into every city and town in America. Dino and Mary often stopped by Mary's parents' house while the Uproars were practicing. He watched them play in the garage. Dino gave the drummer tips on how to improve his technique. As Ralph's drum skills improved, so did the rest of the band's skills.

All seven of the Jr. high schools in the area had garage bands that performed for their school dances. Each year, every school had a Battle-of-the-Bands contest for their local garage bands. The winner at each of the seven schools got to compete with the other schools' winners to claim the region's top prize. The top winner got the unbelievable honor to have three of their songs played on the AM radio by the town's favorite disc jockey, Big Andy Jackson. If The Uproars won, they would get to do six promotional events with the radio station. The Uproars entered the contest feeling confident. They had already won over fans playing at their school's dances. The girls loved them and treated them as if they were already topping the radio and song charts.

The day of his school's Battle-of-the Band contest, Bob carried his base guitar and heath-kit amplifier into the school auditorium. He and his band members scanned the students sitting in the bleachers waiting for the contest to begin. Every student in the school seemed to be there, along with a lot of parents and younger siblings. The Uproars sat in the bleachers and watched the other bands compete. They understood that the competition was fierce. The entire auditorium resounded with intense clapping, feet stomping, and whistles at the end of each band's song. By the time the Uproars got up to play, they knew they had to play their best to win. They busied themselves setting up their equipment. Bob had taken the time to dress in his best hip clothes - black pants, black boots, and a tight-fitting black T-shirt. His thick, brown hair was combed back away from his face, but as he leaned over and plugged in his amplifier, it fell over his face. He pulled his fingers through his hair to brush it back, but it fell again in his face. He stood up and gave it one final swoop back. The girls were watching. Bob outwardly ignored them but inwardly hoped they would notice him. In the past two years of his parents' absence, he had grown tall.

At almost six feet tall, he was the tallest of all the Jr. High kids, and people could not help but focus on him.

When they finished setting up, the Uproar band members took their places. They readied their fingers on their instruments. Ralph bounced a bit in his chair and wove his drumsticks through his fingers to loosen up. Bob felt a jolt of energy rushes through him. He gave the other band members one last glance and nodded his head to signal the start of the song. He hit the opening base note to the Beatles' song, Day Tripper. Immediately, Ralph took charge of the beat. John and Gordon chimed in. Bob and Gordon harmonized the lyrics to perfection. The audience screamed, but Bob did not pay much attention. He focused on hitting all the right base notes and singing his vocal part. The song happened so fast, so quick, that it seemed like he had just taken one breath and the song was finished. The last note reverberated throughout the auditorium. Bob let his hair fall into his face, then lifted his head to the stands and felt his first tear of joy ever run down his cheek, hidden by his lustrous hair. He knew the band had clenched the winning spot. He was right. They won.

The band practiced relentlessly all week for the final Battle of the Bands' contest against the other schools' winners. Ralph's sister, Mary, was thrilled to see her little brother competing for the big prize. As the Uproars practiced in Ralph's garage, rehearsing their songs, in walked four guys, dressed in trench coats, black boots, and belt buckles. They sat down. The entire Rascals' band members had come to help Dino's girlfriend's brother's band rehearse for the big Riverside band competition. They listened to them practice their songs. When the Uproars finished their songs, one by one, the Rascal members assisted the players in developing better techniques to enhance each song. Some of the tips they offered were minor changes that would help them accentuate their delivery. Felix Cavalier, the keyboard player, encouraged them and taught them one by one little tricks to improving their playing. He brought the band's sound together and made it all work in perfect harmony. His approach was to make the Uproars the best they could be. By the time the Rascals were done, the Uproars had added riffs and techniques that spiced up their songs. Felix taught them to use the song, Day Tripper, to introduce themselves. By the time the contest day arrived, the Uproars had perfected their technique and elevated their performance to a professional level.

Bob never entertained the thought of the band becoming famous. He knew from his childhood experiences not to hope for too much in life, to live day-by-day, work hard, and not to smile, unless like now when it was impossible to suppress the bubbly feeling he felt as he stood on stage at the final contest. He and his band members overlooked a packed-full of community onlookers. He pulled the guitar strap around his neck and adjusted his base guitar to fit his body and hands. His guitar was tuned perfectly. The entire Rascals' band members sat in chairs at the front of the stage. The bleachers fanned out to reveal everyone he had ever known in Riverside, including all the music store guys, The Bobby Harrison Trio, who rarely attended these kinds of events, were there to cheer him on.

The announcer leaned into the microphone and said, "The next band in our competition is called the Uproars from Riverside Jr. High. Good luck, boys. Take it away!"

Bob leaned into the microphone. "Hello, Riverside, Rhode Island! We are The Uproars, and we're here to entertain you!" He immediately strummed his first base note to Day Tripper, extending it the way the Rascals had taught him, then broke into the riff. The entire band hit their parts and the energy of the song sent the audience screaming. Bob concentrated on getting every note to resound with energy and drive, to lead a coordinated effort to bring the song together in the best way possible. His notes blended with the drummer. The piano and lead guitar carried the song. They had perfected their harmonies and blended their voices. When they were finally finished playing their three songs, the Uproars walked off the stage, their heads high, the audience clapping and whistling.

On the sidelines, they watched the other bands perform. Bob saw that the competition was fierce, but he hoped they would win. The Uproars had done all they could to clinch the winning prize. At the end of the competition, there was an intermission as the judges decided who would win the prize. Bob mingled with his friends, looking handsome in his black slacks, black boots, black shirt, his brown hair longer than the other band members who still had their parents monitoring their appearances.

When the judges went to the front of the stage to announce the winner, Bob and his band members stood off to the side, where all the participating bands had gathered. Only one of the seven bands would win the top prize. Bob stood erect and looked at the judges. He believed the Uproars to be the best school band in Providence.

The judge, the band leader at the high school, approached the microphone. He leaned into it and opened his mouth. "The winner of the all-school battle of the band contest is…" he hesitated for a moment, then jubilantly said, "The Uproars!"

Bob and his band members could not contain their excitement. Everyone around them was hitting their backs and congratulating them. The Rascals stood and clapped. The audience thundered in response. Bob's band had won. They were the number one school band.

The best part was yet to come. As winners, they got to play three of their songs on the AM radio. They would get to do six promotional events with the radio station. They were going to be famous. All of Rhode Island would know their names. Best of all, Andy Jackson, Big Ange from WJAR, would be the disc jockey to kick off their publicity on the radio. Everyone knew and loved Big Ange for his ability to light up the radio with his contagious enthusiasm.

The Uproars were instructed to go to the radio station. There, they met with Big Ange. The band set up their instruments in the studio and waited until Big Ange instructed them to play. He was in the back booth, the microphone at his lips, the record turntable nearby. Big Ange was larger than life on the radio. He could smooth talk so fast and drag the vowels out in a way that soothed the listeners and energized them at the same time. He signaled to the band to get ready to play.

He leaned into the microphone, "This is big Anggggggg coming to you, Providence, Rhode Island! Today we have for your listening pleasure the winners of the battle of the band contest! You've been waiting for this all night. Call and tell me what you think of them. This ladies and gentlemen, is the Uproars!"

Bob hit the beginning note to the song, Day Tripper, and the band launched into the song that won the hearts of the judges and Rhode Island over. They had rehearsed so much that each note had been planned and now executed to perfection. They harmonized the parts. The song came alive. Bob felt as if his band was bringing the town back to life. He knew this moment would be something he would always remember and cherish.

For winning the Battle of the Bands contest, the Uproars attended six different town events, where live radio disc jockeys introduced the band before they played their music. One was at St. Mary's Catholic School, an all-girls school. WJAR set up their live-radio show outside on the school grounds and Big Ange introduced the Uproars. "We're at St. Mary's school and we are with the Uproars, playing live." Bob hit the base note and the song, Day Tripper, rang out to all the Catholic high school girls dressed in blue plaid skirts and white blouses. The star-struck girls began clapping along, bouncing and dancing. Bob noticed the nuns off to the side, talking amongst themselves, shaking their heads.

When the band finished their song, Big Ange said, "There you have it, folks. The number one band in all of East Providence! The Uproars! They are mighty good and we are so excited to be bringing them live to you at St. Mary's school today. Get ready because here is another song from them."

Bob launched into the song, My Girl. As he played, he watched the school principal walk over to Big Ange and talk to him. Bob and the band members hit every note on their instruments and sang their harmony. Bob was elated. The schoolgirls clapped, stomped their feet, and freely danced around each other.

When the song was done, Big Ange put a record on the turn table, turned it on, and called the band over to him. Bob set his base guitar against his amplifier and followed the band members over to the area where Big Ange had set up his mobile radio station.

"Listen guys, "Big Ange said. "It's not your fault or even your problem. But you got to pack up and go. See those nuns over there with the principal?"

Bob and the band turned and looked at them.

"Well, they do not want an all-boy band playing at their all-girl Catholic school and they do not want any integrated bands playing here either. I am sorry but you have to pack up and go home."

Bob looked at Gordon, the black piano player. Bob put his hands on his shoulder. "They don't deserve us, is what it is. Come on, boys. We have better places to play."

Bob took the lead and began packing up their instruments. The girls stood by the stage, giggling, and looking quite embarrassed by their blushing crushes on the band members. Bob turned and smiled at them. He believed the school did not like the impact they had had on the growing schoolgirls. And Bob did not want to play anywhere that would not accept their black band member.

The next gig with Big Ange was at the Tweet Balzano Restaurant in Bristol. The Italian owner offered an all-you-can-eat spaghetti family night on Friday nights and invited the radio station and the Uproars to play there. The restaurant's picnic-style setting was the perfect atmosphere for families to gather around the picnic tables to eat bowls of homemade spaghetti. The Uproars played for the parents and children who jumped up and danced to the music. Bob could hardly contain his excitement as he played, hitting the base notes, and swaying along on the stage. Never had he been happier.

After they played, the band members climbed into Bob's white convertible and drove around town, whooping and hollering with joy, listening to WJAR, waiting for the chance to hear their songs played. Driving through Riverside, Bob was on top of the world.

The Rascals went on tour in New Jersey and invited the Uproars to be their road stage crew. Bob and the guys were eager to be a part of the Rascals' tour, because all the Rascal band members had embraced and encouraged them. The road days were long, but every night Bob and his friends eagerly set up for the performances. Since the band had already worked many nights at the Alhambra Ballroom helping Burt set up his concerts, they were skilled and ready for the job. In each town, a local band opened the show and played for 30 minutes to warm up the audience for the Rascals' concert. One night the local band canceled. One of their members was sick and the band would not play without him. As the time for the show approached, the producer panicked.

"Why don't let these kids play?" Felix Cavalier said. "They're good."

"They're just kids," the producer said.

"They're good!" Felix insisted. "Let them play."

"They can't play! They're very young, and they have a black organist in the band. I can't put a band on my stage that has a black player." The producer walked away, pulling at his hair. Five minutes before the show was to begin, he became distraught.

"Let the kids play," Felix said. "They just won the battle-of-the-bands. They have been on the radio."

"All right, all right." The producer threw up his hands and stormed off the stage.

"Get ready to play," Felix called to Bob and his friends.

Quickly, Bob and his band members picked up the instruments, turned the amplifiers on, and settled behind the keyboard and drums.

"What's the name of the band?" the producer asked.

"The Uproars," Felix said.

"The Uproars? What kind of a name is that?" the producer said.

'They're good," Felix said.

"Anything but the Uproars! We need something fresh!"

The curtain opened. Felix stood on the stage. He took the microphone. "Ladies and gentlemen! Have we got a show for you!" He clasped his hands together and leaned into the crowd. "Straight out of Riverside, Rhode Island! Something Fresh!" He raised his hand to introduce the band, smiled broadly at them, and then walked off the stage. The crowd broke into thunderous applause.

Bob hit the base notes for their opening song, Day Tripper. The band played for thirty glorious minutes. Bob and his friends played all the songs they knew. Standing on the stage with all the teenagers looking onward, Bob realized he had come a long way away from his early days, when he was kept in an attic or slept in the trees. There was no stopping him now. The band took the house down!

CHAPTER 22

When the tour was over and Bob returned to Riverside, he bought a Triumph motorcycle, souped it up to be a popular chopper bike with long handlebars and a long, comfortable seat, and drove it all over the town. The police pursued him, their sirens blaring. With his shirt flapping off his backside, Bob careened down the road. The police chased him in circles around the blocks. Bob laughed hysterically. He turned down his parents' driveway and drove to the back of his parents' house. He killed the motor, got off the motorcycle, and threw a blanket over it. Then he ran to the front of the house. He sat down in a lawn chair.

A police officer pulled up and stopped. He rolled down his window and said, "I got you."

Bob leaned back in the chair. "For what? I've been sitting here all day."

"I saw you!"

"It was the other guy over there," Bob said, pointing down the road.

"We're going to catch you," the police officer said.

"Who you gonna tell? The chief of police?" Bob knew the chief-of-police had a soft spot in his heart for Bob. So did the neighbors. Although annoyed, they fiercely protected Bob, even if it meant tolerating Bob's wild rides.

Bob traded his 1957 Chevy for a 1967 blue Plymouth GTX that was a ready-to-race muscle car. The engine was blown when he bought it, but that did not deter him from buying it. He brought it to his parents' house to work on it. He used his chain-fall pulley hoisted over a branch of the maple tree in his parents' front yard to pull the blown engine out of the car. He spent $3,000 on the racing engine parts. Using the pulleys, he then lifted a 675-horsepower engine into the car. The car had originally been built with cast iron motor parts. Bob figured if he replaced the cast iron motor parts with aluminum parts, he could cut the car's load in half. So, little-by-little he rebuilt the car using aluminum.

When the car was done, he took it out to race it on the roads. Every time he punched the accelerator, he lost control of the car. If he went fast, the car spun out. He could not steer it. He asked his friend, Margie, to watch him race it down the street and tell him what she saw happening to the car when it spun out.

After she watched him, she said, "How can you steer when the wheels are off the ground?"

Bob realized he had a big problem. He wanted to fix it. He attended the car races and saw that when the drivers punched the gas pedal on race cars at the start of races, the front ends lifted. This automatically slowed all the cars down. Using his ingenuity, he made a suspension mechanism by attaching a plate to the rubber part of a hammer and securing it to the rear axle of his race car. This simple invention allowed his car's front end to sit on the ground and the back end to lift when he punched his gas pedal, sending the car quickly on its way.

Bob entered high school a year later than he should have. When he received his final Jr. High report card, all the teachers had signed its cover. "Great job," Bob." "Loved having you in class!" "I'll miss your special stories!" were just some of the notes that had been written on his report card.

But Bob was reluctant to attend high school and wanted to drop out. He had outgrown every boy in the school and stood over six feet tall, far taller than all the boys in his class. He had spent a few amazing weeks that summer on tour with the Rascals. When he returned, he worked on cars, buying and selling them, and went to old man Ed's shop to help him with his tune-ups and brake jobs. He had visited Giovanni's family and spent his extra time working at his restaurant. He was living a life as an adult, making all his own choices, and could take care of all his living needs.

He enrolled in East Providence High School, bringing the necessary paperwork to school with his forged parents' signature and selected his classes. He was already sporting a mustache and light beard, dressing like a young adult, wearing smart-looking black boots, driving a hot rod car, and looked out of place among his other classmates, who were still transitioning from childhood to adulthood. Although feeling too old to attend high school, he had promised Giovanni and old man Daft that he would attend school. He always kept his promises.

His earlier days when he stood outside of businesses just looking for someone to help him were over. In the beginning of his abandoned years, he had loitered around East Providences until people came out to check on him.

"Hey, kid, what-cha doing out here all by yourself? You need something?"

Little Robby had shuffled his feet, put his hands in his pants' pockets, and shrugged. He had been scrawny, thin, and hungry, with fearful eyes. The business owners had taken Bob in, given him food and jobs, and had looked out for him. The community men called him, "Little man" whenever they saw him.

"How you doing, little man?" they asked. "Did you go to school today?"

"Yes," Bob said.

"Good! Keep it up," they said.

But now he was tall, confident, and painfully aware that he was not cut out to be a scholar like some of the other kids.

On the first day of high school, Bob drove his hot-rod car into the teachers' parking lot and revved the engine to announce his arrival. When he was satisfied with his glaring entrance, he parked his car and got out. He shut the door.

A man approached him. "Hey, kid. Where did you get that car?"

"It's mine," Bob said.

"You old enough to drive?" the man asked.

Bob shrugged. He did not answer.

The man walked around the car, peeking inside it. "Did you fix this up?"

"Yes," Bob said.

The man looked at Bob and nodded. He looked surprised. "What's your name?"

"Bob Begin."

He held out his hand to shake Bob's. "Fred Tiolis."

Bob shook his hand. "Nice to meet you." Bob released his hand and turned and walked toward the school. When he got to the school steps, he turned and looked back. Mr. Tiolis was standing by his car, watching him.

Bob walked to the head office to see where he was supposed to go. When he told the desk clerk his name, she said, "Hold on." She walked to the adjacent principal's office and returned with him.

He looked at Bob. "Mr. Bob Begin?"

"Yes, I am," Bob confirmed.

He placed his hands on the desk and folded them. "Your Jr. High English teacher spoke to me about you. She said you are quite the storyteller. She said you wrote entertaining fantasy tales in your journal but had also revealed the nature of your life. She advocated for you to have a modified high school education."

Bob looked at the principal. He did not respond. The clerk handed Bob his classroom schedule.

The principal smiled. "This is your daily class schedule. For now, you will attend regular classes. But we will keep in touch. Stop by any time and let me know how you're doing."

Bob took the schedule. "Thank you." He glanced at it.

"I hear you are quite musical, so I enrolled you in the band. You are also enrolled in Meister's Singers program. You have math and English and science classes."

"Thank you." Bob turned and left. As he walked down the hallway, he towered over the other classmates. He was fifteen years old. His hands were empty, but the other students carried notebooks. He had arrived at school unprepared for the first day, but he had his schedule. He headed to his first class.

Bob was not interested in his classes. He was too busy earning a living to complete his homework, but he had promised his bosses he would attend school, so he did. He loved playing the clarinet in the band and singing baritone in the Meister Singers' group. The fall season progressed. Bob maintained his steady routine and followed through with his commitments.

He had grown accustomed to his family being absent from his life. It had been three years since they had lived permanently in the house. They occasionally came for weekends, sometimes staying for a week, but they always returned to Maine as soon as possible. His older sisters had gone to college. His brother was working in town. His father's job, building cabins on his land, had taken more time than they anticipated. Bob had not seen his father at all when they had come home for brief visits. If he came home after work and saw his father's car parked in the driveway, he knew not to go there. He slept in his cars or in Giovanni's restaurant on the wrap-around, leather seats. When his parents left again and he returned to the house, he checked the secret box in his mother's dresser drawer for anything she may have left him. Often there was an envelope with a few dollars in it. Bob had religiously left his report cards in the box to show his mother he was attending school.

One Saturday, he went to his parents' home, showered, and then sat down at the kitchen table to eat a peanut butter and jelly sandwich. As he ate, he was deeply engrossed in the race car magazine he had bought at the local magazine stand. He did not hear his parents' car pull into the driveway. He did not hear them slamming the car door shut after they exited the car. He did not hear them at the back door. Suddenly, the back door flew open and in walked his father. Bob quickly turned and looked at him. It had been three years since he was this close to his father. In that time, Bob had grown into a man, six feet, three inches tall and sporting a beard and mustache. His hands were now as large as Uncle Irving's massive hands and were stained with car oil and grease. Immediately, Bob thought about his van that was parked in the driveway. With one quick glance at his father's face, he saw that his dad was furious.

His father made fists. "What are you doing in MY house?"

"Your house?" Bob shook his head.

His sisters, Paula and Alice, were behind his father. His mother came in behind them. When she saw Bob, she abruptly stopped.

"My house!" his father said. "I was hoping you were dead by now."

Bob could not help but laugh.

"The last thing I want is to see your ugly face." His father lunged toward Bob.

His mother reached for his father's arm. "Stop it, Charles. Leave Robby alone." She tugged on his arm sleeve, pulling him away from her son.

His father turned around and slapped his mother across her face. She flew backward, falling into her two younger daughters. The three of them fell against the refrigerator.

Bob stood, enraged that his father had assaulted his mother and hurt his sisters. He towered over his father. He lunged at him. He grabbed his arms. With one strong shove, he pushed his father against the kitchen wall. The force was so strong, the refrigerator shook. He lifted his father's feet off the floor and held him there. He leaned into him. His father tried to kick Bob, but his feet swung back and forth uselessly. Bob pinned his father against the wall and pushed his head into the wall.

"You ever touch my mother again, I'll kill you," Bob yelled. Rage gripped him. Nothing his father did would ever hurt him again. "You hear me. I'll-fucking-kill-you." His mind flashed back to the time when he was a child and his father had dangled him off the floor by his wrist and enjoyed watching a young, helpless boy kick and try to save himself. Now he understood that he was stronger than his father. He took pleasure in his father's sudden helplessness. He held him longer against the wall. Only his mother's crying brought him to his senses. He dropped his father to the floor, stared down at him. A wave of disgust rushed through him. He was the stronger one now. His father could not touch him. If he wanted to, he could really hurt him. But seeing his mother and sisters frightened looks hurt him worse than all the abuse his father had inflicted on him. He looked at his father one last time. Then he bolted out the door, got into his van, and spun down the driveway. He was gone. For good.

Bob was too old to sleep in his cars and his platform treehouses. He needed to find a place to live, and he needed to get his money and guitars out of his father's attic before his father found them. In town, there was a for-rent sign on a ground-level apartment in an old Victorian building. Bob knocked on the adjacent door and talked to the owner of the building. He was an immigrant who did not speak fluent English and did not think to ask Bob his age. He just wanted his weekly bill. Bob agreed to rent it and pay him seventeen dollars a week. The man gave Bob his apartment key. Bob went into the apartment. His first reaction was that the apartment was huge. In old Victorian style, the large living room had a huge front window. The kitchen was in the back, and three big bedrooms and a bathroom were down a long hallway off the living room. Bob immediately took a shower and then checked out the functionality of the kitchen. The refrigerator worked. The oven and stove-top worked. There were plenty of cabinets, which he would never use. The sink was large, and water poured from its faucet. He looked inside the bedrooms and saw he would have plenty of room to store his large bins of car parts. He thought he would sleep in one of the smaller bedrooms and turn the master bedroom into his car shop.

He needed his money that was stored in his parents' attic. By this time, he had hundreds of dollars hidden in the floorboards and walls of the attic. All of it was in cash. He had worked nonstop for the past three years while his parents were in Maine and his only necessary expense had been food, which he mostly got free at Giovanni's restaurant.

But he could not go to his parents' house and risk running into his father. So, he waited. At the end of one day, he went to Giovanni's restaurant to visit Giovanni and the workers and eat dinner. The restaurant felt like home, and he loved running into Giovanni's family, who occasionally went to the restaurant to eat. With them, he had made his first intimate, family connection. He had proved himself to be a hard-working young man, and Giovanni had been more of a father to him than his own father was. The family was eating dinner and when they saw Bob, Mrs. Giovanni motioned for Bob to come sit next to her.

After he sat down, Mrs. Giovanni leaned in and kissed Bob on his cheek. Then she pinched it. "All this healthy food has made you into a man. Look at you - so strong and tall."

"Thank you," Bob said. His mood immediately lifted. He fell into the ambiance of their warm affection.

After he spent a couple of hours with them, he went to his parents' backyard and climbed the same tree he had climbed when he was a little boy to hide from his father. There he waited, perched on an old platform he had built. Finally, his father came out the backdoor, climbed into his truck, and backed out of the driveway. He was gone. Bob swung down a willow tree branch, clumsily now that he was grown but doing it for nostalgic-sake and walked to the kitchen door. He slightly knocked. Through the window, he saw his mother sitting at the table drinking some water. He walked in and greeted her. When she saw Bob, she smiled.

"Robby!" She stood. They embraced.

"How are you, Mother?"

She released him and looked up at him. "I am happy now. Happy to see you. How are you?"

"I'm great, Mom. How long is dad gone?"

"Long enough for you to get your stuff out of the attic," she said. 'But sit down for a bit and tell me how you've been."

Bob sat on a chair.

"He won't be gone long," she warned.

"He can't touch me now," he said.

She sighed. "I have my troubles with him. That's nothing new. But Paula and Alice are doing well. We came back so we can enroll them in school."

"They've grown so much." Bob could hear them giggling in Nancy and Terry's old bedroom. "They probably don't remember me."

"Sure they do," she said.

"It's nice to see you." Bob missed his mother very much.

"You've grown tall and handsome."

"Thank you," he said.

"Just finish high school, Robby."

"I will."

"Promise me one thing." His mother took Bob's hand. "Don't be like your father."

"That's a promise. The counselors at school know what's going on with me. They bring me in regularly to check on me. I told them about my father. They said I should never have children of my own. They say I'll do the same to my own children."

His mother looked sad. "Did they?"

"Their words just make me want to be a father more than anything. I would never do to my children what my father did to me," Bob said, elevating his voice. "I would love my kids. I'd cherish them."

"I know you will. Your father doesn't deserve you, son," she said.

"Darn right."

"I believe in you. I always have."

Bob fought a tear that threatened to fall. "I'm doing great, Mom. I have the respect of our community."

"I know you do."

Bob scanned the kitchen counter looking for a homemade pie. He didn't see one. "Got any pie?"

His mother affectionately patted his knee. She smiled wide. "I made you a lemon meringue pie and hid it in the back of the refrigerator." She jumped up and hurried to the refrigerator. She leaned down and pulled out the magnificent pie. She put the pie on the counter, got a plate, knife, and fork from the cabinet and cut Bob a large slice of it. She put it on the plate, lifted it, and brought it to him, as if she were bringing him the most delicious food in the world. She placed it in front of him.

"Thank you." Bob picked up his fork. "I've waited a long time for a piece of this pie." He pierced the lemon gelatin topped with crusted, beaten egg-whites, lifted the piece, and brought it to his lips.

"I knew you'd come back to see me," his mother said.

"I will always come to see you, Mother." He dove into eating. He wanted to savor every morsel. "Have you been singing, Mother?"

She smiled. "Every free moment I get." She watched him eagerly devour the pie.

Bob wished he could hear her sing again, but the moment didn't seem right for that.

"Promise me one thing," she said.

Before she even said it, Bob knew he would do whatever his mother wanted him to do.

"Promise me you will tell the world your story. The world needs to know. It is your duty in life. We all have our duties. I didn't fulfill mine. But you must." She suddenly looked sad.

Bob nodded. "Yes, I will." He thought about the time four years ago when his mother had lain in bed and refused to get out. She had even spent some time in the hospital. She had stayed in bed, looking old and defeated, but now, looking at his mom, he saw that she had recovered. Her facial skin wasn't pale but bright again. He saw resignation in her expression, a little sadness in the way her lips dipped, but her eyes showed compassion and understanding. She had recovered her life, if not happy, at least resigned to her life.

They both heard his father's car moving along the gravel driveway. They looked at each other. For a moment, they both sat rigid. There were so many more things they wanted to talk about, that they needed to talk about, but now they would not be able to. Bob reached for his mom's hand and squeezed it. His mother got up, hid the pie in the refrigerator, and quickly washed the plate and utensils. He stood and raced up the stairs and went inside the attic. Just as he turned the lock, he heard his father walk into the kitchen, his mother greeting him, and then silence.

Carefully, Bob stepped around the attic. He knew where every loose floorboard was, every hidden crevice in the floor and walls where he had stashed his money, and every low ceiling spot that he accidentally bumped into over the years. Like a quiet mouse, he inched along the floor planks, hoping not to make a sound that would alert his father that he was home. Bob had locked himself in the attic and his father could not get in. Bob sat on his mattress and looked around the dark, small attic. He breathed in the smell of old wood and the musty air. Dampness still permeated the room. The dark wood along the floor and walls made the room, without any lightbulbs, even darker than he remembered it. The sink near his mattress looked even smaller than it had when he was a child. He remembered stealing the pea pods from the neighbor's garden and filling the sink with water. He had made little, handmade pea-pod boats and bombed the boats with the tiny peas he had extracted from inside the pods. Rust had collected on the bottom of the unused toilet, but Bob was sure it worked. No one ever came into the attic but him, and he hadn't stayed up there for a few years now. He remembered lying in the bed and staring at the ceiling, feeling lonely. He remembered how the mattress had aided and comforted him when he was sore and bruised from his father's violent slaps. He remembered performing shadow-puppet shows, perfecting his stories and his act until it was so good, he hosted shows for the neighbor kids for just a seven cents' fee. He looked at the walls and remembered the pirate fights he had with his shadow friend against the candlelight, his newspaper pirate hat and a sword made from wood stolen from his father's cellar, wood shop. This was the place where he had begun to be the person he became.

He lifted himself off the mattress and stood. He walked around the attic. He kept a small box full underneath the floorboard, and with delight he pulled it out and opened it to see all the money that was there. He walked around the attic, pulling cash out of openings in the walls and even the ceiling. He knew where he had hidden all of it. He had been hidden away from his family but not his freedom, not his own life which he had slowly carved out for himself with the help of the community.

He sat on the mattress and organized all his cash. He separated bills into piles of hundreds, then twenties, then tens, then fives, then ones. He separated the coins. When he was done, he stood and stuffed the bills in his wallet until the wallet was bulging with money. He dropped the coins into his pants' pockets. Then he went to the small window and looked outside. He noticed the neighbors' garbage cans along the side of the houses and remembered digging through them for items for his button box, finding half-eaten food that he had devoured and little treasures he had collected. Two blocks down, he saw the break in his friend's fence that he crawled through to reach the Saucony woods where he

built all his platform houses and hidden rusty cans full of his
belongings. He was only fifteen years old, but he felt like he
had lived a lifetime, fishing in the local streams and ponds
for fish to eat, lying on beds of soft leaves, running scared
through the Boston streets, fearful of everyone around him,
jumping the flat-bed rail cars to save himself and make it
home. Funny, he thought. It wasn't the abuse that he had
focused on. He had focused on surviving. He looked out the
window at the small houses in his neighborhood, the clothes
tacked along the neighbor's clothesline. He wished he had
some worms to place on the windowsill for the birds to eat,
just so he could watch them again. It had not all been bad.
He recalled the school counselors telling him he was so
damaged he would never make a good father, that he would
abuse his own children as his father had abused him, as his
father's parents had abused his own father. Bob knew right at
that moment that he wanted to have his own boys. He knew
instinctively that he would never hit them, that if they did
something unacceptable, he would get down to their level,
wipe their tears, and talk to them gently. That was the way it
was supposed to be.

   He turned away from the window. It was late now.
The room was dark. He did not need any light to know
where to go, and which floorboards were firm enough for
him to securely step on and walk along. In the corner, he
picked up the guitar Joe Luca at the music store had given
him when he was just nine years old and went to the door.
He lifted the floorboards and lowered himself down the back
of the stairs, dropping lower and lower, squeezing the guitar
between his legs, his hands navigating the wood as if he were
a monkey in the trees. When he dropped to the cellar floor,

he made his way across the woodshop, which now looked messy, since he no longer cleaned it. He went to the cellar door. He opened it and stepped outside into the dark night. As he walked through the neighborhood, he knew he would never go to the attic again.

CHAPTER 23

The high school principal, under Fred Tiolis' advice, enrolled Bob in the brand new Vocational technical program for kids who wanted to work in a trade instead of attending college after graduating high school. Bob was given the opportunity to attend only morning classes and then attend the vocational program for the remainder of the school day. His high school English teacher allowed him the same privilege the Jr. high school English teacher had given him and told him to draft stories in class instead of doing the regular classroom work. Religiously, he attended his band class and his chorus class.

Fred Tiolis oversaw the vocational school. He liked Bob because his mechanical aptitude was far superior to all the students he had in the program. By the time Bob arrived in his program, he was already a skilled car mechanic. Bob kept a large box of miscellaneous items and used the items to repair the cars he worked on in Mr. Tiolis' shop-class. He could build anything just by thinking about how he wanted to do it. Fred Tiolis became his mentor.

Every day when Bob arrived at his program, Mr. Tiolis asked Bob, "How are you today? Did you get anything to eat? Are you taking care of yourself?"

Bob responded affirmatively. He had plenty to do. After school, he went to old man Ed Daft's garage and did brake jobs on his cars. He often went to Crescent Park to see Burt Sugarman, who always gave him something to do. He went to Giovanni's Italian restaurant for the best spaghetti dinner in town and washed a few dishes for him, and helped him around the restaurant wherever he was needed. At the music store, he cleaned the musical instruments in exchange for music lessons. He knew all the restaurant owners in town, all the Vietnam Vets who took him under their wing. He bought old cars, fixed them by getting parts from the junk yard and then sold them for cash. If not for Mr. Tiolis, high school would have become unnecessary for Bob.

One day, Bob skipped attending school. He loitered with some of the other students on the side of a school building. Fred Tiolis left his classroom and went looking for Bob. He found him behind the building with the other kids who had ditched school that day. Everyone was smoking cigarettes except Bob. The stench of cigarette smoke bothered him. Mr. Tiolis marched up to Bob, took him by the arm, and dragged him away.

"You hang out with those kids, and you'll get in trouble," he said, yanking him. "You are not going down that route. You are extremely talented with a promising future."

Bob looked at him. "To tell you the truth, I was thinking of dropping out of school. I do not need it."

Mr. Tiolis shook his head. "Don't do that son."

Bob shrugged.

"I am going to make sure you come to school every day. I don't want you dropping out."

Bob reluctantly continued attending school. He listened and did as he was told.

Mr. Tiolis watched him make sure he was coming to school every day. After a couple of weeks, he took Bob aside. "I've got you a deal."

Bob's interest was piqued.

"In the morning, you attend your math class. You no longer must attend your English class. All you are required to do is turn in a story every week to your English teacher. At 9 a.m., you come into my shop and work here until noon. Then you hop the fence and go to the Ford dealership garage next door and work there until 4 p.m. "

Bob was stunned. He had always dreamed of working in Mr. Tasca's garage. Now he was going to be given the job of his lifetime. He would be working for the greatest car dealership in all of Rhode Island.

"No drugs. No alcohol. No cigarettes," Mr. Tiolis said. "Stay clean. Remember, you have a great future. Don't mess it up."

"Deal," Bob said. Nothing was more important to him than cars.

The Ford dealership was just a hop over the high school fence and across the street. As Bob walked toward it, his eyes focused on the huge showroom, the windows that circled the building, the attached garage behind the showroom where the cars and trucks were repaired, and the rows of new cars alongside the building. How many times had he walked past the dealership and admired the new cars and trucks they had on display for sale? He loved the new Mustangs, especially the convertibles. Mr. Tasca was also widely known for being involved in the racing car industry, supplying both racing cars and money for the drivers he sponsored. Anyone who was anyone in Riverside went to the Ford dealership if they wanted a new car.

Once on the property, he looked at the new Mustangs, the huge trucks, the shiny red painted cars, the white cars, the blue ones. When he reached the front door, he swung it open with a little too much emphasis. He walked in. He stood in the showroom next to a brand-new sporty Mustang. He walked around the showroom wondering where he should go. Finally, a salesperson pointed him toward Bob Tasca's office. Bob slowed down considerably as he approached his office. At the doorway, he stopped and ran his fingers through his hair. This was the chance of a lifetime for him, and he did not want to mess it up.

He leaned in the doorway. "Mr. Tasca?"

The middle-aged man looked up from his desktop. He lifted his eyebrows and looked at Bob. Then he waved Bob into his office. "Aww, yes. You must be Robert Begin."

Bob stepped into his office. "Yes, sir. I'm here to work for you." Bob noticed photos of Mr. Tasca's family perched in fancy frames on his dark, polished desktop. On the wall behind the desk were numerous photos of racecars and other luxury cars.

Mr. Tasca leaned back in his large, brown leather chair and crossed his arms. "I've heard good things about you."

"Really?"

"A lot of people vouched for you. Ed Daft told me all about you. He says you do brake jobs like nobody's business. Mr. Tiolis says you're a good, honest kid with great mechanical aptitude. Giovanni thinks you are his best employee. Burt Sugarman says you will work all night and all day to get jobs done."

Bob was surprised. He did not know how to respond. Finally, he said, "Yes, I enjoyed all my jobs."

"Come on. I'll have you fitted for your uniforms."

Bob followed Mr. Tasca through the showroom. Mr. Tasca walked like a man who had lived a life of luxury. His immaculate, tailored, black suit did not hide his pudgy stomach. He was as tall as Bob. They met eye-to-eye as they walked. Mr. Tasca took Bob to a room and had the secretary fit him into his uniform.

When they were done and the secretary left the room, Mr. Tasca said, "Fred Tiolis told me about your life and circumstances. The school told me you were a Riverside kid."

Bob didn't respond.

Mr. Tasca continued. "You'll be in the used car shop." He walked Bob to the mechanic shop. Mr. Tasca stood, rubbing his clean-shaven chin, looking around.

Bob scanned the shop. Over the past couple of years, he had grown accustomed to old man Daft's cramped shop, the walls packed with tools, the building old and minimally maintained, the winter months cold, but Bob Tasca's shop was long and clean. Heaters warmed the shop as the mechanics worked under the car lifts. In the corner, was a racing car that was obviously ready to race. Bob had not attended many car race events but looking at the race car, he had a feeling he would now.

"This is where you'll be working," Mr. Tasca said. "Hey boys," he called loudly. "Come meet your new mechanic apprentice."

The mechanics peeked out from under the cars and acknowledged Bob. "Hello! Welcome!" they said.

"Monday, I expect you to come right here after your classes, at noon," Mr. Tasca said to Bob.

Bob nodded. He could not wait.

Monday, after Bob was done in the vocational tech shop at school, he drove his van to the Ford garage. When he walked into the garage, he met the other mechanics.

Mr. Tasca led Bob to the station where he would be working. There was a car lift and a wall for his tools. "This is your workstation. If you need something, just ask the other mechanics."

Bob went to his van and opened it. Mr. Tasca followed him and looked inside his van at the carpet stretching on the van floor all the way to the ceiling, the sink faucet handles for the windows, the oven knobs for the dashboard.

"Love how you customized your van," he told Bob.

"Thank you. I did it myself." Bob reached for his tools.

"I can see that." Mr. Tasca smiled. He hesitated for a moment. "Listen, Bob. When I was young, I was on my own too. I know you are orphaned."

Bob hesitated for a moment. No one had ever used the word orphan to describe him before. For a moment he was embarrassed, but then he recovered and looked at Mr. Tasca. Bob had always considered his platform trees his safe place, even the attic his home. But here was Mr. Tasca, the richest man in all of Rhode Island, the racecar king, dressed in tailored suits and shoes that shone with the kind of shine only money could buy, telling him about his own childhood abandonment. Bob swallowed hard. Suddenly, he understood how the town saw him. They saw him as an orphan. Of course, Bob's circumstances were evident to everyone who knew him. But Mr. Tasca's words resonated with Bob. He saw that his childhood circumstances were not going to prevent him from achieving a good future.

Bob carried the first bin to his new station and placed it on the floor. He went back to his van and got the next tray and carried it to his workstation and put it on the floor. Then he got the last trays out of the van and put them next to the other trays on the floor. He went back to the van and shut the back door. Mr. Tasca followed him back into the shop. The trays were full of used car parts he had found in the neighborhood junkyard and in the dilapidated cars behind old man, Ed Daft's shop. Bob spent time separating all his parts into the proper bins. He organized it so that he knew where each bolt, screw, and spring was in each bin. When he was finished, he began working on his first car. When he needed a part, he got it from one of the trays he had brought into the shop.

Mr. Tasca stood on the sidelines watching Bob replace the brakes on a car. He crossed his arms and smiled. "Just so you know, all the parts that go into our cars must come from the certified parts' department. No used parts in my cars."

"Of course." Bob thought about what Mr. Tasca said for a moment and then decided he liked the idea of using new parts to fix cars. He smiled, realizing he had just graduated from old to new.

CHAPTER 24

Bob was signed up for classes in high school, but he was not required to attend them. Once a week, he turned in a paragraph he had written into the English teacher. He worked on drafting a story entitled "Birth" and added a paragraph to it every week. He chose the theme, birth, because he remembered when his baby sisters had been born and how much their birth and infancy fascinated him. He visited his math and science teachers once a month and talked to them briefly. Just for engaging with the teachers from time to time, they pushed him through their classes with a passing grade. But Bob remained in the band and choral classes and religiously attended a part of Mr. Tiolis' shop class. Every day, as Bob left his class, Mr. Tiolis would tap on the side of his nose to remind Bob to keep his nose clean when he was not in school. For Bob's part, he was getting from the school all that he needed to move into a career once he graduated. It was enough to keep him in school.

The East Providence Meister Singers scheduled a public concert. It was advertised in the newspapers. Everyone was invited to come. On the day of the concert, Bob took his place on stage to sing with his fellow students. The lights dimmed; the audience became quiet. The choral director took her place on stage, lifted her arms, and the choir began singing. Bob sang his baritone part as richly and fully as he could. In the back of the theatre, he watched a woman come inside and walk down the aisle. He could not mistake his mother's steps, the way she leaned forward as she walked, her steps short and slow. She stepped into an aisle, wiggled her way past other guests, and sat down in an empty seat. For a few seconds, Bob stopped singing. A kick from a fellow student on the back of his leg brought him to his senses and he began singing again. He saw his mother clear as day with her short hair billowing around her forehead, her arms folded over her lap. Bob recovered his voice and began singing like he had never sung before. More than ever, he wanted to please his mom and show her that he loved music as much as she did, that he had not forgotten her mellifluous voice that had filled up their house when she had sung to all of them, that he understood how singing made people feel better. As he sang, he made sure to hit all the right notes, and use the right voice tone to blend in with the other voices. When the concert was done, the audience resounded with thunderous clapping, his mother among them. He stood erect and strong, unsmiling but feeling satisfied. With his fellow choral members, he stepped off the stage. He walked right to his mother.

When he reached her, surrounded by other parents, he said, "Hello Mother."

"Oh, Robby," she said, a smile forming on her lips. In the faded cotton dress she wore, she looked out of place among the other moms who wore fashionable pantsuits. "I heard your voice loud and strong among all the singers. You sounded beautiful."

Bob wanted to throw his arms around his mom and bury his head in her neck, to hold her tight and never let go, but he stood like a man, unsmiling, unable to express his feelings. He managed to say, "Thank you."

"I heard you were singing in the choir, and I had to see you. I saw the invitation signs posted on the store windows." She glanced at the other parents, who were moving in the direction of the exit.

"I'm glad you came," Bob said.

None of the other parents bothered to look at his mother. They did not know her personally. She rarely left her home, except to run to the grocery store. They saw her hanging wet clothes outside on the clothesline, or sometimes working in the yard, but she didn't often visit with neighbors. Bob took her arm and led her out the exit and onto the outside sidewalk. Silently, they walked to her car.

When they reached it, she said, "Your father isn't home. Do you want to come home for a bit and visit?"

Bob imagined going home with her, sitting at the kitchen table, enjoying a slice of her apple pie, and listening to her sing as she made the dinner. He longed to say yes, to steal a moment with his mother, but he couldn't. He was already late for work. Bob shuffled his feet through the small, roadside stones. "I can't, Mom. I have a job. I have to go to work."

She looked disappointed but she smiled. "I see." She stood looking at her son. A long moment passed before she spoke again. "You've grown."

"I have new clothes, new shoes." Bob lifted his foot and showed her his black leather shoes. They were already a little worn, and since he had seen her last, he had grown another shoe size. "I'm going to buy new ones soon."

"You have done a good job taking care of yourself," she said. "I wish things weren't this way."

Bob shrugged. "I'm fine, Mother."

"Yes, you will be fine," she said.

He wanted to tell her all about his life, his jobs, and the band he played in with his friends, but he remained silent.

"I'll see you soon." She patted his shoulder.

Bob turned and walked away. He did not want to let Mr. Tasca down. He had to go to work. He glanced back at her one more time. She was standing still, watching him, clutching her purse. She lifted her hand and waved to him. Bob waved back. Then he sprinted to the Ford dealership.

Working at Mr. Tasca's shop improved Bob's life in ways he never imagined. Not only did he make money, but he became a skilled mechanic. The other mechanics teased him and called him the "hacker" because he objected to buying new parts for the cars he fixed, but adhering to Mr. Tasca's requirements, he installed only new parts and then took the old parts home for himself.

On Friday, Mr. Tasca told Bob he wanted Bob to run an errand with him on Saturday. "Come by my house at 9 a.m." He gave Bob his address. "I need you to drive your van."

"Sure thing," Bob said. "I'll be there."

The next morning Bob rose early, took a shower, and combed his hair. He ate donuts for breakfast. Then he got into his van and drove to Mr. Tasca's estate in Barrington, Rhode Island, where Mr. Tasca lived. He had no idea why Mr. Tasca needed him and his van, but he would do anything for Mr. Tasca. The night before he had cleaned his van, wiped down the dash, the oven knobs he had installed to turn on the radio, the station dial, and the sound level. He washed the carpet. The temperature was going to be warm enough for them to roll down the van windows to let the breeze in. He followed the directions Mr. Tasca had given to him to his estate. He drove by the large homes with manicured lawns. He drove by the ponds he had fished in when he was young. He glanced at the tall grass he had hidden in, saw the trees he used to climb. Looking at the huge homes that lined the street, he could not imagine living there.

He turned onto Mr. Tasca's driveway and stopped at the locked gate. Mr. Tasca lived in a mansion, the size of a high school. For a moment, Bob stared at the opulence of the property, the house with its looming front pillars that stretched from the porch to the roof, the yard dotted with flower gardens. Huge trees brought a majestic feel to the land. A ten-foot wall wrapped around the property. Even before Bob hit the intercom button to announce he had arrived, a team of barking, teeth-glaring German Shepherds came running toward Bob's van.

Bob hit the button. "This is Bob. I am here to see Mr. Tasca."

Mr. Tasca came out the front door, a woman behind him. The gate opened.

"Come here," Mr. Tasca called to the dogs.

They abruptly aborted their run and stopped. They stood still as Bob entered the estate. He was surprised by Mr. Tasca's appearance. At work, he dressed in the finest clothes. He wore silk ties, tailor-made suits, and the finest leather shoes made in the world. The cars he sold were the highest quality cars in the nation. When the new Lincoln Continentals arrived at his shop, he fine-tuned the cars. He smoothed out all the door seams. He reworked the engines, transmissions and customized the interiors with new designer colors. He sold them as blueprinted Lincoln Continentals. Everyone who had money wanted one. His impeccable reputation was nationwide. People came from all over to buy one of his special Lincolns. So, Bob had been surprised when Mr. Tasca asked to go for a ride in Bob's old 1961 supped-up van. He was even more surprised when Mr. Tasca walked out his front door wearing blue- jeans and a flannel shirt.

The woman looked at Bob's van and frowned. When she saw Mr. Tasca open Bob's van to get inside, she yelled at him, "Don't bring that young man home for dinner unless he shaves."

Mr. Tasca got in Bob's van, shut the door, and waved her off. "That's my wife."

"Where are we going?" Bob asked him.

"Drive to New Bedford. I need to pick up a foreign shipment from Brazil at the shipping port."

"Ok." Bob put the van in drive and drove out the driveway and onto the street.

Mr. Tasca leaned over and put a hundred-dollar bill in Bob's shirt pocket.

Bob loved his 1961 Ford Econoline blue van. When he bought it, it had a 6-cylinder engine that sat between the driver's seat and the front passenger seat. It was concealed by a lid that completely covered it. Bob wanted a faster van, so he removed the engine and installed a V-8 engine in it. But the lid between the driver's seat and the passenger seat no longer fit over the larger engine, so Bob just left the top off and exposed the engine. Bob's friends called his van a rust-bucket and said you could get tetanus riding in it.

But now Mr. Tasca was in the van, and he was smiling ear-to-ear with pleasure. As they drove, Bob kept his hand on a lever he had installed on the open carburetor. He pulled on the lever and ran the gas through the engine to speed the van up.

"This is great." Mr. Tasca leaned back and laughed.

Bob drove over some sand on the street. The sand flew up into the engine and dispersed into the cabin and onto their clothes.

Mr. Tasca laughed even more. He rolled down the window and let the air clear the cabin. "You sure know how to build your cars."

Bob flew down the street. He had adopted the attitude that he never had to explain why he did things the way he did them. And Mr. Tasca did not question him. Mr. Tasca continued laughing, acting like a teenager himself. As they entered the interstate, Mr. Tasca played with the kitchen knobs Bob had installed on his dash. He turned the radio dial to a rock music station and cranked up the volume.

"I like your van. I especially like the way you hot-rodded it up." He took a cigar out of his shirt pocket, put it in his mouth, and lit it. He took it out of his mouth and placed it in Bob's mouth. He laughed at the sight of Bob smoking the cigar. He lit one for himself, took a long puff, and then blew it out. He hung his arm out the window.

Bob laughed. Never in a million years had he expected Mr. Tasca would go cruising with him. But here he was, sitting next to him. They smoked and flew down the interstate.

Mr. Tasca leaned back in the seat. "You know, I had nothing when I was a kid. I had to make it on my own, just like you. I opened the used car lot in Bristol. Made a million and then opened my own dealership."

Bob listened. He had never thought much about what he would do with his life. He lived day-by-day in survival mode, thinking only about making enough money to survive. But now he wondered. He knew whatever he did in life it would involve something mechanical. He loved creating mechanical things, especially cars.

"You're going to do fine," Mr. Tasca said, as if he was reading Bob's mind. He took a puff on his cigar and cranked up the radio even higher. He bounced to the beat, snapping his fingers.

They both laughed like wild teenagers, zooming past the slower cars down the interstate. Relaxed and happy, they let the fast ride invigorate them, the van a testament to their freedom and their ability to live life on their own terms.

Mr. Tasca pointed ahead. "Take the next exit."

Bob exited the freeway at New Bedford and drove to the ships' loading dock. They parked the van on the dock. While Mr. Tasca arranged to have the large containers loaded into the van, Bob waited nearby. He stopped the engine, exited, and opened the back van doors. Mr. Tasca opened one box. An imported vase with a huge lion sculptured on the side of it was exposed. He opened another box, which had an elephant on it. There were four vases in all, each with a large different animal sculptured on it. Bob secured the vases inside the box and then closed the boxes. He enlisted some deck hands to help him hoist the boxes into the van. Then he and Mr. Tasca drove to another store and bought four banana trees and dirt to plant in the planters. They stopped for lunch and ate a hamburger and French-fries.

Then they drove back to Mr. Tasca's house, still in a jovial, wanderlust mood.

At Mr. Tasca's house, Bob pulled up to the front door, maneuvering the van to avoid the German Shepherds. Then he helped Mr. Tasca and Mrs. Tasca unload the planters, place them around the front of the house, and plant the banana trees inside them. The day was late when they were done.

"Why don't you stay for dinner," Mr. Tasca said to Bob.

Mrs. Tasca put her hands on her hips and looked at her husband. "He cannot. Remember? I said he could not stay for dinner unless he shaved, and he has not."

Bob had never been refused a meal for not shaving. If being rich meant looking the part, he decided that he wanted no part of that.

One day, a 1964, marron-colored Lincoln Continental was brought to Mr. Tasca's dealership and parked next to the mechanics' shop. Bob left his workspace to look at it. He walked around it, admiring the size, the exterior, and the interior. He touched the car, running his hand along its side, wishing he had a car like that.

Mr. Tasca stood in the distance, watching him. Finally, he approached Bob. "You like that car?"

"Yes, I do. It's really a nice car," Bob said.

Mr. Tasca reached into his pocket, pulled out the keys, and handed them to Bob. "It's yours now."

Bob looked at the keys. He looked at the car. He could not believe it. "Are you sure, Mr. Tasca."

"You bet I am. You earned it."

Bob did not know what to say.

That car is a big steamboat," Mr. Tasca finally said. Bob smiled. "It sure is. Thank you."

On the weekends, Bob drove the Lincoln around town. His friends climbed into the front and back seats, and they went cruising along the Riverside roads, the windows opened, their arms out, feeling the wind slap at their hands, whooping, and hollering, as if their newfound freedom needed to be expressed to everyone they passed on the road. For the first time, Bob had a car that didn't use old kitchen parts to make it work. And the car had been a gift from one of the greatest car dealers in all of Rhode Island.

At his apartment, Bob spent a lot of time organizing his auto mechanic shop in the master bedroom. He loaded the hardwood floor with bins full of springs, washers, nuts, and bolts. He stored car engines, pistons, manifolds, motorcycle chassis, tires, wheels, and motorcycle frames all around the room. He saved everything he found and never threw anything away. He brought home any machine part he found. He planned to build a motorcycle in the apartment.

He bought a television and set it up in the living room. He bought a big, quadra-sound system and record player, lots of albums, and cranked up the music to listen to his favorite bands. He brought his friends to the apartment to party and drink beer. The apartment was loaded with cockroaches and mice. Bob and his friends made cardboard mazes to put the mice in to watch them run around it. They each selected a mouse and a paint color, then dropped a dot of paint on their selected mouse's back. Then they watched the mice race through the maze and made bets on which one would win. Bob, although only 15 years old, was content with the life he was living.

Bob owned a small Ford Mercury comet, six-cylinder car. Bob decided to install a faster engine in it. He built a 427 cubic engine on his kitchen table and told his friends he would use the car to drag race. He spent $3,000 on the internal engine parts to build the engine that had 675 horsepower, which would really give his little Ford the capabilities he wanted in the car. He wanted it to go fast. He took out the original engine and installed the new engine, connecting it to all the other parts, making it all work and function smoothly. This was his best car ever. With the new powerful engine, the car would be unstoppable in a drag race. He drove it around the block, revving the engine, punching the gas pedal, and hanging onto the steering wheel as he peeled away from the stop sign.

One evening, he took his friends for a ride. They drove around the neighborhood in a spirited fashion.

"Let's see you do a burn-out on the highway," they said to Bob.

Bob drove to the highway that ran past old man Leonardo's farm, the same farm Bob and his friends had snuck onto when they were kids. They had sat in the trees and when his cows walked underneath them, they leapt from the trees onto the cows' backs. Bob had eventually made friends with Leonardo and fished for crawdads in his farm stream, in exchange for promising to keep his friends away from Leonardo's cows. Over the years, Leonardo had struck up conversations with Bob. They got along very well. Bob told him all about going to his Uncle Irving and Aunt May's farm for the summers when he was younger. Leonardo showed Bob around his farm, and they exchanged farm stories. Bob told him that Uncle Irving had taught him to survive in the woods and that Bob often went to the woods to hide. Sometimes Leonardo invited Bob to eat dinner with him.

Now Bob imagined his delight at racing past old man Leonardo's farm. He thought Leonardo would hear his car as it peeled down the interstate. Bob had shown Leonardo his other cars - his van and his Lincoln Continental, and he just knew if he raced down the street, Leonardo would know it was him.

Bob stopped the car and let his friends out. They ran to the side of the highway to watch Bob race his car. This would be a test to see exactly how fast the car could go with the new engine. Bob looked at the highway that stretched ahead. He steadied himself in the driver's seat. His emotions soared as he revved up the engine. He took a deep breath and then popped the clutch. He pushed the accelerator all the way to the floor. The car took off, spinning its wheels. The back end lifted. Smoke poured off the wheels. The noise was deafening. Bob raced down the road, completely focused on the road in front of him. Then he noticed the car's hood seam was beginning to open. In front of the windshield, a large gap appeared. Bob had no time to react. Suddenly, the entire front end broke off from the rest of the car. The severed nose careened to the right. The wheel axle broke in half. Still in the driver's seat, Bob struggled to control what was left. He hung onto the vibrating steering wheel. The car veered toward the median strip, the car screeching and blazing along the cement with so much force that Bob's entire body trembled. He thought for sure he was going to die. The car flew into the grass and rolled over and over, tossing Bob around, his body slamming into metal, then the grass, then back into the metal as he rolled. When the car finally stopped, Bob was on his side with his face in the grass. The front of the car stretched all the way across the street, the wires and hoses still attached, the headlights shining on him. All of Bob's friends ran away.

Bob lay, stunned. The grass was inside his mouth and nose. He moved his arms and legs and saw he was all right. Suddenly the car rolled over one more time onto its roof. There it sat, pieces of it stretched across the road. He crawled out of his car and stood up. He looked around. He was alone. He was too shocked to know exactly what he should do, so he just stood there.

Bob heard old man Leonardo coming down the road toward him, driving his two-cylinder tractor with chains hanging from his tractor and a large forklift mounted to his front end. He looked at Bob and saw he was all right. He jumped off the tractor and clipped the loose hoses and wires. He hooked the car's front end to the chains. They both jumped onto the tractor. Leonardo hoisted the front end onto the forklift. He drove it up the long drive to his farm. They unloaded it at the back of the barn. Then they drove the tractor back to the accident site and got the back end of the car and lifted it onto the forklift and brought it to the back of the barn. They unloaded it next to the other car parts. Leonardo went into the barn and brought back a huge tarp and covered the entire car with it. Just as they got it covered, the sirens came blaring down the road. Bob and Leonardo watched the police stop and look around for the accident.

They called up the drive to Leonardo. "Did you hear a car crash here?"

"No." Leonardo crossed his arms and watched the police search the area. On numerous occasions, Leonardo had talked about his frustrations with the police. He did not think the police should be bothering the good citizens of Riverside.

The police got back in their car and drove farther down the road. Leonardo looked at Bob and they both laughed. Bob walked back to his apartment. Two days later, Eddy Daft went to old man Leonardo's farm and towed the damaged car to Bob's parents' driveway. He put it in the back of the house. He put the car together to make it look like it did not completely break apart. But the damage to the car was obvious. When Bob went to the house to see the car, his mother was understandably upset.

"Please be careful, son," she told Bob.

"I am." Bob walked around the car, looking at it. The engine had been too big to put inside the small car. The frame could not stay together at such a high speed. He learned his lesson. He got busy taking the parts out of the car. Every part of the car would be saved to be used in other cars.

His mother watched him. She genuinely looked worried.

"See? I am fine." Bob loaded the car parts into his Lincoln and then said goodbye to his mother. "I'll be back for the rest soon." He got in his car and left.

At school the next day, Mr. Tiolis approached him. "I heard about you racing that car and crashing into the median."

Bob was surprised. He did not know anyone knew about it.

Mr. Tiolis looked at Bob. "You gotta keep your nose clean. You can't be driving around doing stupid things."

"Ok."

Mr. Tiolis obviously looked mad but also worried. "Just be more careful."

"I will." More than anything else, Bob did not want to let Mr. Tiolis and Mr. Tasca down. They believed in him.

CHAPTER 25

Mr. Tasca and his family participated in professional drag racing. On Saturdays, Bob went with Mr. Tasca and his family to the car races. Mr. Tasca raced mustangs. The Ford Company had made a racing engine that was immensely powerful but was made of very heavy cast iron. They lost the race.

"This car is over-powered. We are spinning our wheels. I can fix it. We are going to detune it," Mr. Tasca said.

He traveled to the Ford manufacturing plant and had them cast the same engine out of aluminum for him. When he got the new engine installed in his mustang, he tested it on the track. The car was so light that it drove fast.

He signed up to race the car at the racetrack. Mr. Tasca hired a team of highly skilled mechanics to work on the car. Bob was allowed on the team. On race day, the mechanics fine-tuned the aluminum-engine car to make sure all the parts ran smoothly. They shined the brown car's finish and the details on each side that said "Tasca Ford." Then they drove the car to the start line.

When the flag fell, the Tasca Ford took off at lightning speed. People in the stands were ecstatic, cheering, and waving flags. The Ford was far ahead of the others when it passed the finish line in first place. No one knew why the car was so fast. Race after race, the car won. The car became known as the mystery 8.

After they won one race, Mr. Tasca stood next to Bob and said, "I'm the first race car enthusiast in history that has detuned a racing engine to win a race."

They both laughed.

Although becoming skilled as a mechanic at Tasca Ford, using new parts to fix all the cars in Mr. Tasca's shop, Bob maintained his button-box inventive perspective when it came to making his own cars run. In a large bin, he collected motorcycle parts and stored them in his apartment's master bedroom. Someone gave him the parts of a Triumph Bonneville motorcycle. Bob became engrossed in building his own chopper motorcycle. In his free time, he steadily worked on it in his living room. His friend, Rusty, helped him. They built the engine at the table. They assembled the entire motorcycle in the living room, first building all the mechanical parts, then connecting them, making sure they were secured and in top working order. Bob built the chassis, attached the front tire to the long pipes that stretched from the tire all the way up to the curved handlebars. The long seat rested on top of the motorcycle parts. At the back, they put space where Bob could secure his back while he drove it. The silver chrome shone. Bob installed a large headlight just below the handlebars. He modeled the chopper to resemble the choppers in the movie, Easy Rider.

When it was done and they stood looking at it, Rusty scratched his head. The motorcycle was bigger than they expected. "Bob, how are you going to get that motorcycle out of here?"

Bob hadn't thought about that. He looked at the front door. The motorcycle would not fit through the door. "I don't know." Only the large picture window in the living room was big enough to get a motorcycle through. "Let's take the window out."

He and Rusty took the large picture window out, set it against the wall, and placed wood planks down from the window to the ground. Bob went inside, pulled his motorcycle up to the window, sat on it, and then drove it out the window and down the planks. He got off it and pulled the planks away. Then he and Rusty put the window in its proper place and secured it there. After they were done, they both looked at the motorcycle, sitting outside on the driveway. They both burst out laughing.

Bob got on the motorcycle and kick-started it. It sputtered and coughed but it started. He reached his hands to the long handlebars and looked at his friend and smiled. He turned the motorcycle toward the street, revved the engine, lifted his legs onto the pedals, and drove the motorcycle onto the street. He flew through the exhilarating wind, his leather jacket's sleeves flapping, his jeans protecting his legs, his hands gripping the handlebars. He raced along the neighborhood streets watching out for the children, dogs, and cats running around. A police officer on car-patrol heard his motor, found him, and chased him. More police cars joined in the race to stop Bob. But he was not only quick, but he was also clever. He turned off the streets to evade the police, ripping through the neighbor's yards, tearing down clotheslines, spinning his tires through the wet grass, spewing up dirt and mud behind him. Mothers waved their fists at him in anger, but he knew they would not report him. They were the ones who kept him safe in their households overnight when his family had not kept him safe and warm. They had washed his dirty clothes, fed him breakfast, sent him off to school alert and ready for the day. They may be angry now, but they would never tell. Bob knew that as he flew by them on his new chopper. He watched the police cars driving along the streets following him, but he disappeared behind houses, knocking apples off low-lying branches of apple trees, weaving in and out of trees, finally reaching the interstate, where he found himself cruising at top speed, the motor running smooth and strong, the chrome pipes glistening in the sun. He passed old man Leonardo's farm at top speed. Leonardo looked up from his work and peered at Bob. Bob, in jubilant fashion, punched the gas and sped by him, knowing that Leonardo knew exactly what Bob was up to, another button-box masterpiece, created by the one and only lost boy of Riverside, Rhode Island, the boy who obviously had made it.

Bob drove the motorcycle to his parents' house. He wanted to show it to his mom. Usually, his father was at work at this time, but when he pulled his chopper to the back of the house, he saw his father sitting on the steps. Too late to leave, he cut the engine and straddled the motorcycle.

"Hello," he said to his father. For a second, he hoped his father would admire his motorcycle and he could tell him about it, but one look at his father, sitting with his legs spread on the bottom step, eyeing him, and slowly pairing an apple with a small, sharp knife, Bob understood his father was in a foul mood.

He looked at Bob with contempt. "You're going to die on that deathtrap."

Bob shook his head slightly, realizing the conversation was going to go badly.

His father bit into an apple slice stuck to his knife. He slowly chewed. "That'd be fine with me, because if I never see you again, I'd be happy."

Bob cranked the engine on and turned the motorcycle around. He blew out of the driveway and drove down the street. He had already driven two miles on the interstate before he knew where he was going. He had $1,000 tucked in his pant-leg pocket, and he was going to need it. He drove for hours nonstop, north along the interstate, past the towns, the houses, the stores. The traffic getting heavy and then eventually thinning out the farther north he drove. He kept a steady ride, leaning back in his seat, steering the motorcycle in and out of traffic, following the speed limit so he would not get stopped. He did not see many motorcycles on the road, only the muscle-cars with big engines, carrying families, men to work, and vacationers. He drove next to the ocean, seeing the sun shimmering on the waves. He stopped for hamburgers and gas fill-ups, but otherwise kept a steady pace on the road. He reached the Canadian border and crossed into the country he loved.

He had one focused objective – to reach Uncle Irving and Aunt May. It had been a long time since he had seen them. He longed to be on their great Nova Scotia land. As he drove, he thought about the cute Riverside girl he had met in Rhode Island. She had often come by to watch him work on cars. She sat off to the side on a bucket with her elbows on her knees, fists at her chin, and stared at him while he worked. No words passed between them, but Bob had noticed her, and now, as he drove, he thought of her. He had never had a girlfriend, had never thought of dating girls, but now this cute mystery girl captured his mind as he drove.

The road carried on for miles, up the north end, past the long prairie grasses and looming hills, the hidden cottages in the distance, the little gas stations, and stores along the way. He wasn't tired. He felt energized. He longed for the great land and knew his desire would not be completely quelled until he stood on his Uncle Irving and Aunt May's farm, where the birds flew freely through the trees and up to the sky, the bears roamed the land, sharing it with the deer, the rabbits, the wolves.

Finally, he reached Nova Scotia. He headed north along the road that ran along the ocean, the cool wind keeping him alert and awake, his brown hair flying behind him like a banner to his independence. There was no stopping him now. The road was the only civilized intrusion on the land. Bob raced along it, heading east now, winding around the curves with precision, the wild ocean off the cliff sending its waves crashing into the shore. Bob went back in time, not only to his childhood years but back to a way of life that eluded the technological progress America was making.

He saw the road that led up the hill to Uncle Irving and Aunt May's farm. He slowed and turned onto the road. Within minutes, his loud motor announced his arrival. Uncle Irving stumbled from the barn to see what the noise was about. Bob stopped the motorcycle. He waved to his uncle and kicked the stand to keep the motorcycle upright. He leapt off it and began walking toward him.

Uncle Irving put his hand up to shield his eyes from the sun. He stood still. "Bobby-boy, is that you?" He began walking toward Bob.

Despite the stiffness in Bob's legs from riding his motorcycle for so long, he stepped up his pace. "Yes, it's me, Uncle."

"Bobby-boy!" Uncle Irving shouted. "May! May! It's Bobby-boy come to visit!"

The house's front door flew open and out stepped Aunt May. Bob turned to look at her. She clasped her hands to her face. "Bobby-boy!" She ran to him.

By the time she reached him, Bob was already in Uncle's arms. They hugged tightly with a grip on each other that would never let up, as if they were back in time when Bobby-boy had arrived at their house a broken boy, badly in need of love, food, and guidance. Aunt May joined them, and Bob laughed with happiness at the sight of his beloved Aunt. They embraced warmly, the scent of stew and homemade bread lingering in the air around her.

"You're grown!" she said.

Bob pulled away and stood next to Uncle. They stood head-to-head, both six foot, three inches tall, both with massive hands. Aunt May, much smaller than them, peered up at Bob with a wide smile.

"I knew you'd be back," Uncle said, 'but I'm surprised to see the odd machine you arrived on." He laughed. "What is that thing?"

"It's a motorcycle. I made it," Bob said.

"You made it?"

"Come look at it." Bob showed his uncle his motorcycle, going over the parts, how they all fit together to make it drive. He went into detail about how he had collected the motorcycle parts at junk yard, off bicycles, in bins mechanics had discarded. He had filled three bins with the parts used to build it.

"Never in my life," Uncle Irving said. "I ain't seen nothing like this before."

Bob realized that Irving had only seen occasional small airplanes flying above his land and old tractors and old cars.

Irving stood, scratching his head. Bob continued to explain the motorcycle to them. "It's called a chopper."

"A chopper?" Aunt May said, looking mighty confused.

"It's just a word they use to describe motorcycles with long front ends," Bob said.

"That's one mighty machine," Uncle said.

"The world has changed," Aunt May said.

"Bobby-boy, you out-did yourself," Uncle said.

Aunt May looked at Bob. "I bet you are plum worn out after that long ride. Come into the house for some food, then you can rest for the evening by the hearth."

Bob walked his motorcycle to the barn and parked it inside. Then he went inside the house. The smell of stew and homemade bread, the familiar chairs, the table, the hearth, the pots hanging on the wall, the hardwood floors, the beams that ran across the ceiling filled his senses and made him feel happy. Aunt May dished up a generous amount of stew and cut him a large slice of bread. Bob sat at the table and lathered his bread with her homemade butter.

They ate and talked about what had happened in the years gone by since they had seen each other. The seasons had come and gone, the repetitive work of each season accomplished, the horses, the land, the rivers, the trees. It was all still the same. Bob soaked up the familiarity, the love, the acceptance. When they finished eating, Aunt May brought out some strawberry pie and served it. Aunt May looked the same, with her thick, gray hair tied behind her, her floppy dress with big pockets, and the thick, black shoes. She was just a little bent now, but not much. She still walked with a slight, energetic bounce.

Bob relished each bite of the delicious pie. "Just like my moms," he said.

"While you're here, I'm going to need some help around the farm." Uncle's big, thick fingers picked up a large piece of thickly buttered, homemade bread. He eagerly bit into it.

"Sure thing." Bob finished his pie and wiped his mouth. "That was delicious."

Aunt May stood, took his plate, and carried it to the counter. "You look exhausted," she said to Bob.

"I am, and now that I ate that delicious meal, I feel I could fall asleep sitting up," Bob said.

"You go rest," Uncle Irving said. "You can stay in the loft where you used to sleep. In the morning, we can work."

Bob stood. "Thank you." He left the table, climbed the stairs to the loft, and as soon as he lay down on the bed, he fell into a deep sleep.

He awoke before dawn. He sat up. Immediately, he got out of bed, got dressed, put on his shoes, and climbed down the stairs. Aunt May and Uncle Irving were not yet awake. Bob opened the door and went outside. The rooster announced the day. The sun had yet to peek over the hills. Bob went to the horse barn and petted Barney, still as muscular and strong as he remembered him. He left the barn and went for a walk along the trail, following the path he had so often taken as a kid when he spent his summers there. He walked until he was in the wooded area. He looked up at the massive trees he had climbed when he was a young boy. He saw the intertwining tree branches high in the trees, where Uncle Irving had taught him how to make wooden platforms to hide from the animals. He watched the hares running along the ground to get away from him. He walked to the river and watched the sunrise. The orange, red, and yellow rays stretched along the land. Water rippled over the rocks at the edges of the stream. He saw the fish swimming along in it and recalled when Uncle had taught him to fish with just his hand. Bob did not know how to properly thank his uncle for such a precious gift, but he understood the enormous love his uncle felt for him and he for him.

How he loved the feel of the cool breeze, the wet grass soaking his boots, the leaves that wrestled in the trees, the smell of the pines. If he could, he would stay there forever. This was where he felt safe. This was where nature had given him his most important lessons in life. This was where he had learned he could survive. He walked back to the wooded area and climbed a massive tree. He was so seasoned at climbing that it took him no time to scramble up it. He swung his legs down a big branch and sat quietly, looking around at the land, seeing the ocean off in the distance. The wind came to him, surrounding him, calling to him with its pure whooshing sound. Sitting high in the tree, he watched an eagle soar in the sky. He saw the deer walking below him on the ground, watched bears make their way past him, never looking up at him. Nature had taught him to let it be his guide, that everything he'd ever need in life was right before him in the forest, whether here or in Saucony Woods or the millponds or in old Leonardo's stream abundant with crawfish. The great Nova Scotia waterways that fed into the ocean, the land green and plentiful, was all a boy needed to survive. Where there were trees, where there was water, where the land stretched forever, there was an opening for a little, weak, and confused boy to find his way.

Bob walked back to the farmhouse, feeling his stomach rumble in anticipation of Aunt May's breakfast of eggs, bacon, and pancakes. He found Uncle Irving in the barn feeding the horses.

"There you are, Bobby-boy. Come to the house. Aunt May cooked us breakfast. Then we will get to work." Uncle affectionately grabbed Bob's shoulder and walked with him back to the house.

Aww, Bob thought. Here it is. Here is the place he had been looking for. A lightness overcame him. Happiness and joy. Freedom and love. Irving, a man of few words, had guided him. Nature had carried him in its embrace all these years just so he would reach this moment. He took a deep breath of the clean, fresh air and held it in. Here was his home.

Jayne Gongol, a former social worker who directed a literacy program for homeless children, wrote this memoir to demonstrated how positive acts of kindness can save a traumatized child. She is also the author of Where flowers Grow, an American Civil war novel. She resides in southern California.

Made in the USA
Las Vegas, NV
11 August 2023

75950854R00171